BIOLOGICAL TIME

THE MACMILLAN COMPANY
NEW YORK · BOSTON · CHICAGO · DALLAS
ATLANTA · SAN FRANCISCO

BIOLOGICAL TIME

By

P. LECOMTE DU NOÜY

*Chief of the Division of Molecular Biophysics,
Pasteur Institute, Paris; formerly Associate
Member of the Rockefeller Institute*

With Foreword by

ALEXIS CARREL, M.D.
Rockefeller Institute for Medical Research
Author of "Man the Unknown"

New York
THE MACMILLAN COMPANY
1937

PRINTED IN THE UNITED STATES OF AMERICA
BY THE POLYGRAPHIC COMPANY OF AMERICA, N.Y.

TO
DR. ALEXIS CARREL
THE SPIRITUAL GODFATHER OF THIS BOOK
WITH THE AFFECTIONATE GRATITUDE OF THE AUTHOR

FOREWORD

In this book, Lecomte du Noüy discusses an aspect of ourselves, which is both very important and little known—our duration. To endure is an essential characteristic of all living organisms. Time is, in fact, the fabric of life. In his admirable "Creative Evolution," Bergson has shown the fundamental importance of time in biological phenomena. "Wherever anything lives, there is, open somewhere, a register in which time is being inscribed." But the time of our body is not the same as physical time, that is, the time marked by a clock. Physical time is an aspect of the cosmic world. Inward time, an aspect of ourselves. It differs as much from physical time as the solar system differs from a man. It is identical with the living body. For this reason, Lecomte du Noüy has united in the title of his book the ideas of life and time. It is impossible to understand the nature of our time if we ignore the nature of organic phenomena. Time and life are one and the same thing. A better knowledge of human duration will permit a more effective application of the factors of our environment to the development of our physiological and mental life.

Physiological time, like physical time, is the expression of certain intrinsic changes within a system. While physical time depends on the motion of the earth around the sun, inner time is bound to some modifications of our humors and tissues. These modifications constitute aging. Of course, aging is an extremely well known phenomenon. But we have only recently learned how to analyze it. In this book, methods are described for the measurement of physiological time, and for the study of its characteristics. Physiological time has been estimated in two different ways: By the rate of wound healing, and by chemical changes taking place in blood serum. The first method was invented by Lecomte du

Noüy in the laboratories supported by the Rockefeller Institute in France during the Great War, while he was studying the repair of wounds. A constant relation was found to exist between the velocity of wound healing and the age of the patient. From the mathematical formula expressing the repair of tissues, Lecomte du Noüy extracted a constant, which varies from 0.4 for a child of ten years to 0.08 for an old man of sixty. In this manner, age can be detected by rate of healing. The other method, much less precise, is based on certain changes that take place in blood serum. During the course of life, blood serum progressively acquires the power of arresting the growth of tissues when they are cultivated *in vitro*. This change is probably responsible for the decrease, in function of age, in the velocity of the repair of a wound.

The knowledge of physiological time is of obvious importance because it leads to the understanding of its value. Long ago, Minot found that the younger an animal is, the more rapid is the rate of aging. From his experiments, it could be inferred that physiological time has a much greater velocity in youth than in old age. But we remained ignorant of the extent of those differences. Their numerical value has been determined by Lecomte du Noüy. The rate of tissue repair is five times slower at the age of sixty than at the age of ten.

The significance of the time of a clock depends naturally on the characteristics of physiological time. When compared with physiological time, physical time loses its uniform value. Parents and children live in different temporal worlds. They are separated by a gap that often is too large to be bridged, even by illusions. Within the familial group, the individuals should not be separated by too great a temporal distance. It is, therefore, desirable for women to have children as early in life as possible. Again, the knowledge of the characteristics of physiological time teaches us that, at the end of life, aging is very slow. From one year to another, the appearance of an old man in good health hardly changes.

Any acceleration in the process of aging in a senescent individual signifies the incidence of a disease, which should be detected. It also becomes obvious that the value of a day is much greater for a child than for his parents and his teachers. The younger a child is, the richer his life in physiological and psychical values. Such a fact should not be neglected by educators. Every moment of the existence of a child must be utilized for his formation. A clear realization of the enormous value of physical time for children would bring about a real progress in education and in the quality of individuals. The knowledge of physiological time is equivalent to the knowledge of life itself, because time cannot be separated from life. The deeper this knowledge, the more successful will be our approach to the mystery of our self. For these reasons, I am happy to present this book by Lecomte du Noüy to the American public.

Alexis Carrel

Rockefeller Institute for Medical Research, New York

CONTENTS

DIAGRAMS

xiii

BIOLOGICAL TIME

INTRODUCTION

The consequence of the progress of Science is the gradual weakening of all the primary concepts born of ignorance. Their only strength lies in the unknown, and as that is gradually elucidated quarrels must cease, divergent doctrines must fade away and be replaced by scientific truth which will reign supreme.

CLAUDE BERNARD (1875)

THE problem of life has always passionately interested man. And yet there has never been a satisfactory definition of life. Why is this? Perhaps because a distinction must be drawn, as Claude Bernard pointed out, between the word and the thing itself. Pascal, who so well understood all weaknesses and illusions of the human mind, points out that in reality true definitions are creations of the mind, or *definitions of names*, and merely conventions for shortening speech. But he admits that there are primitive words which are understandable without need of definition. According to Claude Bernard, the word 'life' is one of these. Everybody comprehends the words 'life' and 'death'. It is impossible to separate these two terms, for what lives will die, and what is dead has lived.

Ideas on life have necessarily varied with different epochs and according to scientific progress. The reader may remember the purely verbal definition of the Encyclopedia: 'Life is the opposite of death', and that of Bichat: 'Life is the combination of functions which resist death.' In other words life is the combination of the vital properties which resist the physical properties. This is a vitalistic view. It was generally thought that Claude Bernard meant to give a definition of life when he wrote: 'Life is Death.' But this is not quite true for, in a later article, this phrase is preceded by another which is usually overlooked and which materially restrains its meaning: 'If we wished to express the fact that all vital functions are the necessary consequence of organic combustion, we would repeat what we have already stated: Life is death, the destruction of tissues. Or we would say with Buffon: Life is a minotaur; it devours the organism. If on the contrary we wished to insist on this second phase of the problem of nutrition, that life maintains itself only by a constant regeneration of the tissues, we would consider life as a *creation* accomplished by means of a plastic and regenerating act opposed to the vital manifestations.'

Claude Bernard was not the man to be enslaved by a formula, as is proved by his words: 'Facts are always more beautiful than the most beautiful theory.' His keen intelligence dictated the lines which even to-day contain the clearest and truest thoughts on the subject. In the course of this introduction we will only express his ideas, and in spite of the rich harvest of new facts of which he had no knowledge, it will be seen that his admirable common sense, his respect of truth, and his genius still dominate all physiology.

The following pages are extracted from two little-known articles published in the *Revue des Deux Mondes* in 1867 and 1875. Their perusal will show why they were chosen as an introduction to this book.

'At the beginning of the nineteenth century, a physiologist could still publish a volume of experiments *On the Principle of Life and the Seat of this Principle*. We no longer search for the seat of life. We know that it is everywhere, in all the molecules of organized matter. The vital properties are in the living cells. Everything else is but organization and mechanism. The manifold manifestations of life are the expression of thousands and thousands of combinations of elementary organic properties which are themselves fixed and invariable. It is therefore less important to know the immense variety of vital manifestations which nature never seems to be able to exhaust, than to determine rigorously the properties of the tissues from which they spring. That is why to-day all scientific effort is directed towards the histological study of the infinitely small elements which contain the true secret of life.

'No matter how far we delve into the phenomena pertaining to living beings, we are always confronted with the same question which was propounded in ancient days, at the very beginning of Science: Is life due to a power, a special force, or is it only a modality of the general forces of nature? In other words, does life contain a special force which is distinct from the physical, chemical, or mechanical forces? The Vitalists have always claimed the impossibility of explaining physically or mechanically all the phenomena of life. Their opponents have always answered by giving well-proven physico-chemical explanations to an ever-increasing number of vital manifestations. We must admit that the latter have constantly gained ground. Will they succeed in explaining everything by their theories, or in spite of their efforts will there not remain a *quid proprium* of life which will always be irreducible?

'This is the point that must be examined, for, far from being only of philosophical interest, it is, on the contrary, capable of showing us to what degree the fundamental problems of all biology are dominated by chemical and physical methods.

'There are two classes of nutritional phenomena which essentially constitute life and which are the origin, without exception, of all its manifestations. One of these, organic destruction or disassimilation, can already be classified among the chemical actions. These decompositions in living beings are no more mysterious than those which take place in organic substances. As to the second class, the phenomena of organizing genesis and nutritional regeneration, they appear at first glance to be of a quite distinct vital nature, and often irreducible to general chemical actions. This, however, only appears to be so, and these phenomena must be considered under the double aspect of an ordinary chemical synthesis and of an organic evolution in progress. Indeed, vital genesis incorporates phenomena of chemical synthesis arranged and developed according to a particular order which constitutes their evolution. *It is important to separate the chemical phenomena from their evolution, from their correlation in time, for these are two entirely different things.*[1] As synthetic actions, it is evident that these phenomena reveal only general chemical forces. By examining them successively one by one this is clearly demonstrated. The calcareous matter which is found in the shells of molluscs, in birds' eggs, in the bones of mammals, is certainly formed according to the laws of ordinary chemistry during embryonic evolution. Fatty and oily substances are in the same case, and chemistry has already succeeded in reproducing artificially, in the laboratory, a great number of immediate principles, of essential oils and of complex bodies which are the apanage of the animal and of the vegetable kingdoms. Starchy substances which are developed in animals and which reproduce themselves in the green leaves of plants by the combination of carbon and water under the influence of the sun, are also well-characterized chemical phenomena. If the synthetic properties of nitrogenous substances are much less clear, this is due to the fact that organic chemistry is not far enough advanced as yet. But it is nevertheless certain that the substances are built up in living beings by chemical methods. In truth, it may be said that the germs and the cells, elements of organic synthesis, are most exceptional agents. In respect to the phenomena of disorganization it might also be said that enzymes are special factors characterizing living matter.[2] The following seems to be a general law. Chemical phenomena in the organism are produced by special agents or processes. But this does not alter the purely chemical nature of the phenomena which take place, nor of the products which are their result.

'And now we come to organic evolution. The agents of

---

[1] The italics are mine.—L. D. N.

[2] Due to the remarkable work of Gabriel Bertrand, the fundamental role of infinitesimal traces of metals in the activity of the enzymes is now known, but so far it has been possible to synthesize artificially only one of them. (Kuhn, 1934.)

chemical phenomena in living bodies do not confine themselves to producing chemical synthesis of extremely varied substances. They organize them and render them appropriate for the morphological edification of a new being. The most powerful and marvellous agent of this living chemistry is, without question, the egg, the primordial cell which contains the organizing principle of the whole body, the germ. We cannot observe the creation of the egg *ex nihilo*. It emanates from the parents, and the origin of its evolutive potentiality is hidden from us. Science, however, is bringing us every day nearer to the heart of the mystery. It is by the germ, and in virtue of a kind of evolutive power which it possesses, that the perpetuity of the species and the descendance of beings are established. It is likewise the germ which enables us to grasp the necessary links which exist between nutritional phenomena and growth phenomena. It explains, or at least allows us to conceive, the limited duration of the living being. For death must ensue when nutrition stops, not because food is lacking, but because the evolutive sequence of an organism, which must be admitted even though we do not understand it, has reached the term of its career, and because the organizing cellular impulse has exhausted its power.

'The germ likewise controls the organization of the individual by forming the living substance with the help of the surrounding medium, and by giving it the unstable chemical characteristics which are the cause of its unceasing vital movements. The cells, secondary germs, similarly dominate the organization of cellular nutrition. It is evident that these are purely chemical actions. But it is no less evident that these chemical actions, through which the organism grows and is built up, are linked together and succeed each other in view of the result, which is the organization and growth of the individual, animal or vegetable. It is as if a vital drawing existed which traced the plan of each organ, so that even though each phenomenon in the organism is tributary to the general forces of nature when taken separately, when taken successively and as a whole, they seem to reveal a special link. Some invisible contingency appears to lead them in the path which they follow and to impose the order in which they are bound. The synthetic chemical actions of organization and of nutrition thus manifest themselves as if they were dominated by an impulsive force which governs matter, creates a special chemistry appropriated to its end, and brings in contact the blind reagents of the laboratory just as the chemist himself would. We already know that this power of evolution, inherent in the ovule which is to reproduce the living being, covers the phenomena of generation as well as those of nutrition. They both, therefore, possess a basic evolutive character.

'This power or property of evolution, which we can just mention here, would alone constitute the *quid proprium* of life, for it is clear that this evolutive property of the egg, which will produce a mammal, a bird, or a fish, is neither physics nor chemistry. Vitalistic conceptions can no longer reign over physiology as a whole. The evolutive force of the egg and the cells is therefore the last stronghold of vitalism. In taking refuge behind it, however, it is clear that vitalism transforms itself into a metaphysical concept and destroys the last link which bound it to the physical world and to physiological science. In stating that life is the directing idea, or *evolutive force* of the organism we simply express the idea of unity in the succession of all morphological and chemical changes linked together by the germs from the beginning to the end of life. Our mind grasps this unity as a concept which imposes itself, and we explain it by a force. It would be a mistake, however, to believe that this metaphysical force is active in the same way as a physical force. This conceptual force does not leave the intellectual realm in order to react upon the phenomena for the explanation of which it was created. Although an emanation of the physical world, it does not act upon it retroactively. In brief, the metaphysical force through which we can characterize life is unnecessary to science because, being outside the physical forces, it cannot influence them in any way. We must therefore separate the metaphysical world from the phenomenal world which acts as its base, but which cannot borrow anything from it. Leibnitz expressed this delimitation in the following way: "The body develops mechanically, and the mechanical laws are never violated in natural movements. Everything takes place in the soul as though there were no body, and everything takes place in the body as though there were no soul.'"

In brief, if life can be defined with the help of a special metaphysical concept, concludes Claude Bernard, it is nevertheless true that mechanical, physical, and chemical forces are the only efficient agents of the living organism, and that the physiologist must take their actions alone into account. As Descartes says, 'We think metaphysically, but we live physically.'

PART I
THE BIOLOGICAL PROBLEM AND METHODS

CHAPTER I

OUTLINE—BIOLOGICAL METHODS

THE preceding pages give a certain aspect of the biological problem and of its infinite complexity. We do not propose to study in detail all biological problems, but only those which may lead us progressively to the notion of time. If we seem occasionally to deviate from our plan, it is because of the necessity to show that, in spite of the difficulties encountered and of the criticisms that can be made, certain modern methods more than others are capable of helping the physiological sciences, and even medicine, to progress rapidly. We hope that the reader will be left with a truly optimistic outlook.

In order that one may understand the general plan and follow the directing thread between chapters which might easily seem to possess no common link, we must state, at the very beginning, that it is our purpose to introduce a new concept of time, or, more exactly, to try to demonstrate that a fundamental difference exists between physical time, the time of the universe which flows at a uniform speed, and our physiological, internal time, on which, so far, we had only very vague ideas. We will show that this physiological time, which has a beginning and an end, does *not* seem to flow at a uniform rate. We will indicate the possibility of deriving from our own organism a unit of time different from the classical one derived from the rotation of the earth around its axis. We will also attempt to show the quantitative discrepancy between conceptual and physiological time. This will lead to an explanation of the differences perceived in the appreciation of the flow of time at the beginning and at the end of life, and to a hypothesis on the relation existing between the two times.

Now, the point upon which we must insist at the beginning of this book is that all these results are not based on hypotheses but on experimental biological facts obtained by two different methods which mutually check each other. The experimental facts have been studied quantitatively, and our conclusions are often derived from their mathematical relation. We do not start from one or more postulates, but from measurements and velocities. These researches were not undertaken with the object of arriving at a definition of time, but on the contrary in order to elucidate certain very definite biological problems. The conclusions imposed themselves on us when the experimental work was ended. That is why it is necessary to give the reader a general idea of the biological problem and of the methods by which it can be examined in detail, so that he may follow progressively the path which led us to these conclusions. It is important for him to be fully convinced of the part played by the physico-chemical and chemical mechanisms in life phenomena in order to understand, for example, the value of the argument derived from the demonstration of the activity of the temperature coefficient (Van't Hoff constant) in the appreciation of time. It is essential that he should understand the role of the chemical reactions in the organisms. It is indispensable for him to know in detail the mechanism of the cicatrization of wounds and of tissue-culture, so that he can trust the calculations on which the whole work is based, and realize the importance of the quantitative checks on which our reasoning rests. The elementary notions to which we constantly refer will sometimes be briefly dealt with, so as to avoid the necessity for the reader to consult technical books or papers in search of mere definitions.

In other words, we have tried to answer beforehand the principal questions which might be put to us and the objections which might be raised. We are not under the illusion that we have completely succeeded, but we have done our best.

Our plan is the following:

1.   We will show that the modern conception of a living organism enables us to study it from different points of view which can be roughly classed in three groups, each of which imposes a distinct category of methods:

(*A*) From the point of view of its objective manifestations as a whole, that is to say, as an entire organized individual, either isolated or in its normal environment: zoology, descriptive botany, etc.

(*B*) From the point of view of the mechanisms of the biological actions, using what we might call the *breaking-down methods*. Either *dynamic*, i.e. maintaining life and entailing no serious alterations in the part played by each mechanism in particular (physiology); or else *static* methods, which start by destroying life (cytology, etc.).

(*C*) From the purely physical and chemical point of view, namely, by suppressing conventionally the difference which distinguishes living from dead matter, and by incorporating life with our material universe.

In the first case the unit will be *the individual*; in the second, *the cell*; and in the third, *the molecule*. It can be seen that each class corresponds to a different order of magnitude, therefore to different methods of investigation. If we admit the beautiful definition of Ch. E. Guye: '*It is the order of magnitude that creates the phenomena*', we shall be in each case confronted by different phenomena.

2. We will study in detail a fundamental biological phenomenon: *cellular reparation*. First, under its best-known and most important practical aspect, *cicatrization of wounds*; secondly, under the experimental aspect given it by Dr. Carrel: *tissue-culture in vitro*. We will discuss the mathematical consequences which can be derived from the experiments and which introduce a particular concept of age and time.

3. Having introduced quantitatively the notion of time in the experiments previously described, we will develop the subject by explaining the conventional and relativistic concept of time and its classical measurement.

4. Finally, we will develop the concept of *duration* and of physiological time. Contrary to the customary procedure, we will borrow a unit *from our internal time*, and we will use it

to measure the physical exterior time. In other words, we
will confront a time felt and lived, with a time merely conceived. We will thus directly oppose *life*, the subconscious,
to *intelligence*.

The study which first imposed itself on the human mind
was evidently that of *whole* organisms in the animal and
vegetable kingdoms. In principle, this requires neither
laboratories nor complicated apparatus. The old-time natu-
ralists and botanists began by describing what they saw.
The eye, the ear, the senses in general, are the only instruments needed for these contemplative sciences. It is not even
necessary for the scientist to do the observing himself, as is
proved by the example of the great naturalist François Huber,
who although blind left some remarkable experiments which
he conceived on the subject of the life of bees (1814) and
which were executed and seen by his servant, who had
absolutely no scientific ideas of his own. Huber was thus the
directing spirit, but he was obliged to borrow another man's
senses. However, the pure and simple description of nature
does not in itself constitute a scientific work. It leads to a
classification which would be extremely complex and without
significance if it did not seek to establish, behind the different
appearances of individuals, the similarities leading to kinships
which are real even though less apparent. That is why the
observer must be completed by the experimenter. Claude
Bernard wrote at the beginning of his *Introduction to the
Study of Experimental Medicine* some beautiful pages in which
he analysed at length these two forms of activity of the
scientist in general.

'The observer purely and simply describes the phenomenon which takes place before his eyes. The only thing he
must ward against is an error of observation which might
lead him to see a phenomenon incompletely or define it
badly. To this end he will employ all the instruments which
can help him to make his observation more complete. The
observer must be the photographer of the phenomena, his

observations must represent nature exactly. He must observe without a preconceived idea. His mind must be passive, that is to say silent. He listens to nature and writes under her dictation.

'But once a fact is ascertained and the phenomena observed, the idea comes, reasoning intervenes, and the experimenter appears in order to interpret the phenomenon. The experimenter is he who, in virtue of a more or less probable but anticipated interpretation of observed phenomena, institutes an experiment so that in the logical order of his previsions it will furnish the result which serves to control the hypothesis or the preconceived idea. To accomplish this, the experimenter reflects, tries, gropes, compares and combines, so as to find the experimental conditions which are best fitted to attain the goal which is his aim. It is necessary to experiment with a preconceived idea. The mind of the experimenter must be active; that is, he must interrogate nature and question her in all directions following the different hypotheses which are suggested to him.

'But when the conditions of the experiment have been realized and the experiment itself started according to the preconceived idea or anticipated view of the mind, the result, as we have already said, will be a provoked or premeditated observation. It will be followed by the apparition of phenomena determined by the experimenter, but which he must first study so as to know in which way they can be used to check the experimental idea which brought them to life.'

It is clear that these lines apply to all classes of methods and are not confined to the one which is the object of our first paragraph. But it seemed to us that they belonged to the beginning of this chapter because of their evident character of generality.

The naturalist and the zoologist can resort to a variety of methods, depending on whether they study the isolated organism, or whether they consider it as an element of a social whole. It is difficult to study certain insects, for example, without taking into consideration the role of the individual in the superior unity, namely the hive, the ant-hill or the termitarium, inasmuch as the individuals differ largely by their morphological and physiological characters, according to the part attributed to them: warriors, workers, queens, or males.

These observations do not entirely eliminate planned experimentation. The great entomologist Fabre describes ingenious experiments which were suggested to him by the attentive examination of the habits of insects. The naturalist can intentionally introduce an alteration or a disturbance in the conditions of natural phenomena and make *destructive* experiments with the aim of ascertaining *in vivo* the use of organs the functions of which are not evident.

In brief, this class of methods tries to comprehend the organism as a whole. Similar to a jet of water of unvarying aspect, to a stream for ever following the same bed, to the flame of a candle, or to any other system which conserves its form although composed of ever-renewed and ever-fugitive particles, a living being is a system the fixity of which is only apparent. It owes the constancy of its form, of its aspects, and of its mean composition to the evolutive correlation of the phenomena of which it is the seat. But we hasten to add that there is a striking difference between the maintenance of the 'stationary systems' just mentioned and the renovations which are characteristic of the living being. The stationary system is only a witness to the constancy, in time, of an indefinitely repeated phenomenon. According to Ostwald it is the *passive* result of this regularity. On the other hand, nutrition in living organisms consists of an aggregate of numerous, variable phenomena. The ensuing morphological permanence is an indication of the active part played by the organism which is its seat. This activity is all the more evidence that these systems evolve, develop according to a constant order, and reproduce themselves.

The idea of studying individually each of the elementary

endowed with definite characteristics.[1] The characteristics of the individual at a different scale always superimpose themselves on the characteristics of the materials.

'Would a naturalist who had only studied an elephant through the microscope believe that he had a thorough knowledge of this animal?' asks Henri Poincaré.

Thus, on the one hand, we are necessarily led to the physical and chemical study of living matter, for without this analysis the mechanism of the physiological functions would remain a mystery. On the other hand, we must always consider at the same time the organism as a whole, without ever losing sight of the special conditions of all separate phenomena which constitute the individual. There is, therefore, a kind of antinomy between the aims and methods of the medical man and those of the bio-chemist or bio-physicist. This antinomy is only apparent, but it suffices to account for the difficulty experienced in establishing an intimate collaboration between these two disciplines.

In reality, the chemist and physicist seek the elementary phenomenon by cutting up bodies fictitiously into infinitely small cubes, because the conditions of the problem which undergo slow and continuous variations when one passes from one point of the body to another, can be considered as constant in the interior of each one of these small cubes. Their ambition is to establish the law of certain variations. This law has a meaning only on condition that sufficiently simple

---

[1] There is much to be said on this subject, and particularly on the biological properties derived from the increase of the complexity and of the molecular weight of the organic substances. Above a certain molecular weight the definition of the chemical unit, the molecule, does not suffice to characterize *all* the properties of the unit. Similarly in the atoms, radioactivity accompanies the complication and fragility resulting from the high atomic weight. Pigmentary proteins have been found in certain animals (snails) of enormous molecular weight (more than five millions). These immense molecules, if they can still be given this name, are so complicated, that it is quite possible that in these primitive organisms, they function as complete organs. This observation seems to be confirmed by the fact that, in this particular case (hemocyanine of Helix's blood) the molecular weight varies according to the physiological activity. (Roche.)

elements are dealt with, so that the events studied have a chance of repeating themselves. But this would not be possible, as Henri Poincaré pointed out, if instead of ninety-two simple elements we had ninety-two billions of them, equally distributed in the world.

'Then each time we picked up a new pebble, there would be a great probability of its being made of an unknown substance. Everything known about other pebbles would be of no help for this one. In front of each new object we would be like a new-born child. In such a world there would be no science. Thought and even life would perhaps be impossible, for evolution could not have developed the instinct of conservation.'[1]

 The medical man, on the contrary, even though he tries, like the chemist and the biologist, to simplify, to unify, and to generalize with respect to the cells, the body fluids, and the organs, is not the doctor of living beings in general. He is not even the doctor of the human race, but of the human *individual*, and what is more, of an individual in certain morbid conditions which are special and which constitute what has been called his idiosyncrasy. From which it seems that medicine, contrary to the other sciences, must constitute itself by being more and more individualized. (Claude Bernard.)

It is needless to point out that this contradiction is purely artificial and due to the fact that the groundwork, on which the physiologist and, later on, the medical man must rest, is still too frail and too scarce, owing precisely to our ignorance concerning the structure of the chemical elements of the organism. It is therefore necessary first of all to enrich bio-chemistry and bio-physics with facts, so as to supply physiologists with the foundations which are actually wanting.

But this programme, which holds in so few words, gives rise to extreme difficulties not suspected in the time of Claude Bernard.

[1] Henri Poincaré, *Science et Méthode*.

'The brilliant beginnings of organic synthesis,' wrote Jacques Duclaux a short while ago, 'had raised hopes that this chasm which separates physics and chemistry from biology could be crossed by the resources of organic chemistry alone. . . . The oft-employed formula according to which living organisms obey the same laws as inert chemical compounds, dates of this period. The idea that such a formula could have been seriously given makes us smile to-day. Pushed to such a point, optimism is no longer a quality.'

Those who have studied living matter and elementary organisms in the laboratory by means of the most advanced methods of physics and chemistry, and have surrounded themselves with the greatest precautions, know well that everything happens as if 'life was a struggle against the physical laws', as Professor Lapicque puts it. It is not without interest to compare this phrase with that of Bichat, cited at the beginning of this chapter: 'Life is the combination of functions which resist death.' How surprised Claude Bernard would have been had he been told that sixty years later, his successor, instead of having more proofs of what he already considered assured, would on the contrary express himself with far more prudence?

Consequently, from the physical as well as the chemical point of view, one of the obstacles which we have to surmount is the following: we try to apply the laws of inorganized matter to phenomena which are dependent on them without, however, obeying them completely. The deviations which we observe are the measure of our ignorance. Donnan's famous equilibrium is never rigorously found on both sides of a *living* membrane. As far as osmotic pressure is concerned, the cells do not function like a Dutrochet osmometer. The difference of pressure which exists only maintains itself thanks to the work produced by living matter which plays a fundamental part. It is the phenomenon which Lapicque named 'Epictèse'. The electric resistance of a cellular wall falls to one-tenth of its value when the cell dies. (Osterhout).

In brief, the vital equilibria which bring infinitely complex structures into play are never absolutely comparable to the physical and chemical equilibria. 'True equilibrium is death,' said Bayliss.

Now that we have shown some of the pitfalls which the chemist and physico-chemist encounters in his study of living matter, it is only fair to add that a great number of biological problems can be solved by means of chemical and physical methods, and even can only be solved that way. Amongst these, luckily, are those which are of the greatest interest to humanity, namely the problems of immunity in general, protection against infectious disease, as well as a great number of pathological and therapeutical problems. After the preceding rather discouraging pages we will try to give a slightly more optimistic note.

CHAPTER III

CHEMICAL AND PHYSICAL METHODS— LIMITATIONS—RESULTS ACQUIRED—THEIR ROLE IN IMMUNITY AND BACTERIOLOGY

THE difficulties which we have enumerated are important only when we seek to understand the intimate mechanisms of fundamental biological phenomena, the 'irreducible principle' of Claude Bernard. The objection based on the evolution of the notion of determinism is purely theoretical, and in no way changes the results of our experiments. Whenever we try to superimpose an example borrowed from an inert body on to a series of chemical phenomena taking place in an organism, we observe that there is no absolute accord, even though the point of departure and the point of arrival are identical. Usually we are not aware of this discrepancy, as we cannot know the real intermediary stages, but only those which we have ourselves realized. This brings us back to Plato's picture of the cave, in which our senses perceive only the shadows projected on the background. If our problem consists in the exact analysis of the means employed by nature to obtain a certain result, the chances are that our rough methods will fail, until the far-off day when some kind of electronic chemistry will be perfected. Even then we will succeed only if there is no other point of divergence, which is not very likely.

But our ordinary chemistry can render great services if we concern ourselves chiefly with the points of departure and arrival. If, for instance, we manage artificially to obtain substances identical with—or sufficiently similar to—those which determine pathological disturbances, by an excess or deficiency in the organism, we will have truly progressed. We will thus be able to neutralize them if they are too abundant, and to replace them by purified and concentrated or even synthetic products if they are deficient.

37

This is what takes place for hormones amongst others. We now understand the troubles brought about by lesions in the thyroid gland. Any diminution in the secretion of the hormone manufactured by this gland is followed by severe accidents: cretinism, myxoedema, goitre. Physiology brought us this far. Now, biological chemistry has not only succeeded in purifying and obtaining in crystalline form the active principle, thyroxin, which contains four atoms of iodine, but has synthesized this compound artificially. The introduction into the organism of two milligrams a day of thyroxin is sufficient to dispel all morbid symptoms and often brings about a complete recovery. The result is identical, whether thyroxin extracted from organs or the synthetic product is employed and, as these active substances are pure, a minimum dose, which can be indefinitely tolerated, suffices. Chemistry has solved the practical problem which was propounded by medicine and studied by physiology.

This is an example amongst twenty. Up till now, only thyroxin and adrenalin have been synthesized. The other hormones are extracted from organs of animals. But the constant strides made in this direction permit us to look forward to the day when they will be manufactured directly from pure chemicals. In the same way insulin (hormone of Langerhan's islets) renders the greatest services in serious cases of diabetes. It is certain that the mechanism of the production of thyroxin, insulin, and adrenalin in the glands themselves escapes us altogether. But it does not matter, if we have understood the part they play as regulators of certain physiological functions in the organism.

We know very well that vegetable cells chemically fix nitrogen at normal temperature, whereas we can only obtain the same result, *in vitro*, around 500° C. But from a practical point of view the important thing is to understand the role of nitrogen in the metabolism of plants. The rest will perhaps come later.

It might be objected that the practical point of view should not be considered in science. But much as we believe that a purely utilitarian conception of science is as great an absurdity as a utilitarian conception of art, we nevertheless think that in certain cases science has nothing to lose by advancing in a direction which, besides being fascinating by the mystery which surrounds it and by the marvellous complexity and harmony of its objects, may lead to the suppression of suffering and the amelioration of human conditions.

No painter, however independent, would refuse to decorate a beautiful monument. His work can only gain by the grandeur of the frame, and he has no reason to feel limited in his liberty if no one imposes the subject or any other restrictions and if he has the impression of participating in the edification of a masterpiece.

The new orientation of bacteriology is chemical. This impulse seems to have come from Vienna, about thirty-five years ago, with Obermayer, Pick, and particularly Karl Landsteiner, who, by his remarkable and epoch-making experiments, showed the value of this method of analysis for the study of immunity. Should one, under pretence that the intimate mechanism of immunity, the real nature of cellular phenomena, will always escape us—which is not proved— abstain from working in this path which has already enabled us to throw so much light on the secondary mechanisms of fundamental interest to us?

If the physicists and engineers, beginning with Ampère and Faraday, had reasoned in this way on the subject of the nature of electricity we would have none of the comforts which characterize our modern material civilization; neither electric light, telegraph, telephone, nor radio. Waterfalls could not have been utilized. The greater part of modern metallurgical and chemical methods would not have been brought to light. And who knows to what degree a quantity of other industries would not have been hampered in their development. Evidently we can ask ourselves, like Tolstoy and a few others, if this would not have been preferable. But it must be conceded that this is quite another problem, and that man can no more escape the current which sweeps him towards

an unknown fate than a drop of water can travel up-
stream.

We will now try to show what important results may be
obtained by applying chemical and physical methods to a
biological problem, and we will take as an example a problem
of capital importance: immunity.

. . . . .

The experimental work which illustrates our thesis was
chosen not only because of its recent and fundamental character, but also because it represented the last link in a chain
which was started at the beginning of the twentieth century
and forged with scientific rigour and admirable logic by the
scientists whose names we have already mentioned: Obermayer
and Pick and, especially, Karl Landsteiner. The latter, not
long ago, obtained the Nobel Prize for Medicine for his discovery of the four blood-groups. This discovery, as everybody
knows, made blood transfusions absolutely safe. Our choice
was therefore not only governed by the interest of the work
itself, but by the fact that it is solidly based on a long series
of previous discoveries which rendered it possible. It also
enables us to foresee a still longer series of discoveries to come.

We shall now briefly report the experiments of Dr. Oswald
Avery and his collaborators, Drs. Michael Heidelberger, René
Dubos, and Walter Goebel, which represent the perfect type
of research in modern biology. This work was done in the
laboratories of the Rockefeller Institute in New York.

Pneumonia is one of the diseases which cause the greatest
havoc in the United States. In the great majority of cases it
is due to a micro-organism called 'pneumococcus'. We have
known for a long time that there are very distinct differences
in pneumococci which manifest themselves by a characteristic
specificity. They develop in the same way in artificial media,
but even though their aspect under the microscope is the
same, they can be classed in well-defined and specific types
which simply bear a number: types I, II, III, etc. The
differences existing between these types are not revealed by

the ordinary bacteriological methods, but by more subtle methods called *immunity reactions*. These reactions are essentially chemical, and cover all the processes by means of which the body tries to fight against infectious disease. For example, we know that if a solution containing microbes, let us say pneumococci of type I, is injected several times into the veins of an animal, the latter will, as a reaction of defence against the foreign cells, manufacture new substances, called 'antibodies', in his blood. The consequence of this fact is not only that the animal is actively immunized against a subsequent infection of living and virulent pneumococci but that the *serum* (which is the liquid part of the blood) containing the antibodies, confers a *passive* immunity, when it is injected into the body of another animal susceptible to the same infection.

What is more, when the serum of the animal immunized by means of the pneumococci type I is mixed with the same microbes in a test-tube, the micro-organisms act in a strange way. They stick to each other in clusters, in masses. They are what is called 'agglutinated'. These reactions are strictly *type-specific*, that is to say serum antipneumococcus type I only agglutinates the pneumococci type I and has no action on the organisms of another type. It is therefore possible, by employing specific immunized sera of each type of pneumococcus, to classify an unknown culture by the nature of its reaction in contact with one or other of the immunized sera.

I insist on the specificity of the different types of pneumococci and on their immunological reaction thanks to which they can be distinguished, for this is at the base of the work which will now be described.

The biological classification of pneumococci was established before anything was known of the chemical nature of the substances which determine the specificity of the type. Before going any farther we will say a few words on the importance of having a biological classification for the chemical and epidemiological knowledge of the malady. This classification has made it possible to appreciate the frequency of cases of pneumonia due to each type of microbe, to recognize the difference of gravity, as well as the death-toll of the infections which they determine and to understand better the mode of dissemination of the disease, by finding the different types in the mouths of healthy or convalescent individuals. Finally, the notion of 'type-specificity' has provided us with the only rational basis for the production of an immunized serum which has proved its value in the treatment of infections of type I.

In the course of their first experiments, Avery and his collaborators naturally asked themselves: To what could be due this extraordinary specificity, and in what part of the microbe it resided? How could it be possible that organisms so completely identical from a morphological point of view were so different from the point of view of their immunological properties? Previous observations furnished the clues that put the searchers on the road to success.

The pneumococcus is a unicellular organism which is surrounded, under certain well-defined conditions of growth, by an envelope more transparent than the microbe itself, visible under the microscope and known as the 'capsule'. This capsule is particularly well developed in pneumococci which grow and multiply in the body of animals. During their growth, the capsulated cells secrete in the midst of the culture a diffusible substance which, in solution, presents the characteristics of type-specificity of the organisms from which it derives. This substance is found not only in the filtrates of young cultures but also in the humours of animals experimentally contaminated, and in the blood and urine of the patients during the evolution of pneumonia in man. The faculty of elaborating this product increases with the virulence of the pneumococcus, and there is every reason to believe that the capsule of the micro-organism is constituted mainly by this specific substance. Thus, around each microbe, there exists an ectoplasmic layer or capsule capable of reacting with the serum of an animal immunized against the same microbe, the so-called anti-serum. This reaction is remarkably specific and occurs *only* when the anti-serum and the capsular substance are of the same type. The problem, then—and it was a difficult one—was to isolate the substance in question in a pure form, and to determine its chemical constitution and its role in the immunological properties of the pneumococcus as a whole.

The capital discovery that these soluble substances, which are responsible for type-specificity, belong to the family of carbohydrates, that is to say sugars, is due to Dr. Michael Heidelberger, a brilliant chemist and one of Avery's first collaborators. No matter what type of pneumococcus they are extracted from, they always possess in common the chemical properties of the complex sugars, the polysaccharides. But strangely enough, the polysaccharide derived from each specific type of pneumococcus is chemically different, and each one possesses particular properties which distinguish it clearly from the others. What is more, chemically purified solutions of these sugars manifest the same specificity, from the immunological point of view, as the microbes from which they are derived. To give an idea of their astounding activity it suffices to mention the fact that by means of the corresponding serum it is possible to reveal their presence at a concentration of one five-millionth or 0·0000002 grams in one cubic centimetre of solution.[1]

From the point of view of medicine, and especially of serology and immunology, this discovery was of capital importance for two reasons. First, because it had been believed up till then that immunity reactions were solely due to extremely complicated substances the chemistry of which is very little known—the proteins. And second, because by demonstrating that the capsular sugars were as chemically distinct as they were serologically specific for each type of pneumococcus, Avery and Heidelberger brought a striking proof of the close relation existing between the chemical constitution and the specificity of the microbes.

[1] Let us mention that Heidelberger and Avery accomplished the same experiments, with equal success, on types A and C of Friedlander's bacillus. It is interesting to note that 75 litres of an autolysed, eight-day-old culture medium are needed to yield about 1 gram of polysaccharide.

It was a brilliant confirmation of the splendid work of Landsteiner on complex antigenes. His researches led him to conclude that biological specificity is conditioned by chemical groups relatively small with respect to the antigenic molecules. A new proof in favour of this thesis was given by Avery, as we shall see presently.

Thus the specificity of different types of pneumococci depends on the chemical nature of the sugar which forms the capsule. What would happen if the microbe could be *relieved of this capsule*. Would it die? Would it conserve its virulence? Of what nature would be its specificity and what accidents would it occasion in an animal? All these problems were completely solved by Avery with the collaboration of a young Frenchman, René Dubos. But it required several years to do it, as no enzyme capable of attacking, dissolving, in other words, of digesting these sugars could be found. Finally, Dubos isolated from the bogs of New Jersey, a microbe of the soil, which secreted an enzyme capable of digesting the capsule of pneumococcus type III, without killing the cell.

It was now possible to obtain cultures of pneumococci *having totally lost the type-specificity*, deprived of virulence and incapable of invading the animal in which they were injected. However, these microbes had not lost the faculty of surrounding themselves with a new capsule which restored their specific virulence. But it became possible to give these cells the faculty of surrounding themselves by the characteristic sugar of a different type and of transforming themselves into pneumococcus types I or II. A degenerated microbe can produce any kind of specific saccharide, according to conditions in which it is placed.

The authors then had the idea of injecting doses of these enzymes into the bodies of the experimental animals—mice— so as to discover whether they would digest the capsule of the virulent pneumococci *in vivo* and render them inoffensive. They ascertained that their previsions were fully justified and that it was possible to protect mice specifically against type III, and solely against this type.

They afterwards studied the chemico-immunological

properties of the capsular polysaccharides. These sugars are not toxic and do not seem to be responsible for the accidents which accompany a pneumococcic infection. But certain facts indicate that they can indirectly oppose the normal mechanisms of defence against this disease. Indeed, by reason of the avidity with which they combine with the antibodies, they tend to neutralize the substances resulting from the processes of immunization, and thus prevent these protecting agents from reaching the centres of infection. What is more, the pneumococci enrobed in their shell of sugar resist phagocytosis,[1] whilst the naked microbes divested of their capsules are energetically absorbed and destroyed by the phagocytes. We have already seen that pneumococci artificially deprived of their capsule lose their virulence and do not multiply like the others. This is due in part to the vigorous offensive of the phagocytes which devour their enemies bereft of their protective armour. And now we come to a most important point, the crowning touch to the magnificent work which demanded such long years of effort from the scientists of the Rockefeller Institute.

The chemically purified capsular polysaccharides of the pneumococci have lost the power to induce the formation of antibodies in the animals to whom they are injected. In other words, they cease to function as genuine antigenes whilst conserving the faculty of combining with the specific antibodies resulting from the injection of the integral microbe. In this way, they are related to the important group of substances, immunologically active, which Landsteiner named 'haptenes',[2] and which behave in the same way.

As these sugars, these carbohydrates, are antigenic when they are accompanied by the microbic cell, Avery came to the conclusion that in this case they cannot exist as free

---

[1] Phagocytosis, which is the process by which certain wandering cells of the organism surround, absorb, and sometimes digest any invading element, was discovered by Metchnikoff. The 'phagocytes' act as the policemen of the body.

[2] Haptenes are substances which react specifically, but fail to induce immunity (i.e. to determine the appearance of antibodies) when injected into an animal: they are *not* antigenic.

polysaccharides, but under some other form, for example, chemically combined with a protein or another substance which gives them an antigenic power of which they themselves are deprived.

In order to see what would be the consequence of the introduction of a radical 'carbohydrate' in a protein molecule, from the point of view of the orientation of the specificity of the new compounds thus formed, Avery and Goebel chose two simple sugars (monosaccharides), glucose and galactose. These two substances have the same composition and the same chemical formula. They differ one from the other only by their configuration in space, the groups H (hydrogen) and OH (oxhydril) fixed to one of the carbon atoms occupying a different place in each case. Starting from these two sugars, Goebel succeeded in synthesizing the corresponding 'para-aminophenol-glucosides'. Then each of these derivatives of the sugar was combined with a protein (globulin of serum or egg albumin) so as to obtain definite compounds (sugar-azo-proteins), that for simplification can be called galacto-globulin, galacto-albumin, gluco-globulin, and gluco-albumin. Rabbits were immunized with these substances, and the sera of these animals, containing the antibodies, were submitted to immuno-logical reactions similar to those of which we spoke above. It was found that the specificity of each of the compounds thus created, was *solely determined by the radical sugar*, and altogether independent of the nature of the protein to which it was combined. This fact was capital. The introduction of a simple sugar in a protein confers to the entire compound a new specificity which is determined by the chemical structure of the carbohydrate. The sugars in question differ only by the spatial relations of the groups OH and H attached to the fourth carbon atom. A simple rotation of 180 degrees around this atom suffices to change completely the serological specificity of two substances otherwise identical. The marked differences between pathological accidents can then be due to the simple displacement of a chemical group in a molecule.[1]

[1] The similarity between the two substances, the *p*-aminophenol β-glucoside and the *p*-aminophenol β-galactoside clearly appears in the two structural formulas:

Avery and Goebel were thus ready to attack the final problem rich in significance and consequences, the synthesis of an artificial bacterial antigene, obtained by combining the polysaccharide of a pneumococcus with a foreign protein. With this end in view they chose the sugar of type III which, being totally deprived of nitrogen, can be considered as a definite chemical entity and has never by itself determined any immunological response on the part of the injected animal. It is not only inactive in a pure form, but the microbe from which it is isolated does not in the majority of cases possess the power to bring forth antibodies in rabbits.

The great difficulty from the chemical point of view consisted in preparing by synthesis the substance derived from the polysaccharide capable of combining with a protein without neutralizing or masking the chemical groups. This feat was accomplished by Goebel, a young and brilliant pupil of Heidelberger. He obtained the 'amino-benzyle-ether' of sugar type III which he combined with a foreign animal protein, the globulin of horse serum. This soluble antigene has nothing in common with the pneumococcus type III excepting the polysaccharide, and yet the rabbits into which it was injected reacted by manufacturing specific antipneumococcic antibodies in their serum. The serum of these animals not only precipitates the synthetic antigene, but specifically agglutinates the living cultures of pneumococcus type III and

$$NH_2 \diagdown \diagup \diagdown O-C-H \qquad NH_2 \diagdown \diagup \diagdown O-C-H$$

Glucoside	Galactoside
O—C—H	O—C—H
H—C—OH	H—C—OH
HO—C—H	HO—C—H
H—C—OH	OH—C—H
H—C	H—C
H_2=C—OH	H_2=C—OH

It can be seen that the only difference consists in the position of H and OH at the level of the fourth carbon atom.

protects mice against an infection engendered by the virulent microbes of this type.

There are few comments to add. As a result of this splendid work we begin to see the dawn of a new bacteriology and immunology, no longer founded on empiricism but on the scientific knowledge of the mechanism and the chemistry of the phenomena of infection and defence. Progress will be long and tedious, but success is certain, for the path is now traced, and though bristling with difficulties it is the only one open to us. And if we remember the methods and principles of Pasteur, chemist and physicist, we realize that it follows the true Pasteurian tradition.

.   .   .   .   .

We have thus far taken a bird's-eye view of biological problems in general. In studying the methods of investigation we have pointed out a few of the difficulties that are encountered. Some are of a purely material nature, mostly due to technical difficulties of all kinds resulting from the inadequacy of methods created to solve the problems of inorganized matter when applied to living matter. Others are of a deeper nature; concerning either the problem in itself or else the mechanism of our thought and the criterium of our reasoning. Finally, however, we succeeded in convincing ourselves that at the base of our normal or pathological physiological reactions, chemical phenomena existed that could be approached by our techniques. They are, if one might say so, the material foundation of life, but not life itself.

Now that we are in possession of these necessary premises we can proceed to the study of a biological phenomenon of fundamental importance, as it is one of the manifestations of the tendency to persist which characterizes living beings. It is one of the rare problems which can actually be submitted to measurements and calculations, and which, as we will soon see, allows us to introduce time quantitatively in the shape of a variable depending only on the organism as a whole.

phenomena which contribute to the edification of the living being as a whole is therefore quite natural. No matter how much a motor is tampered with, one cannot hope to know how it works without taking it to pieces. This brings us to the second class of methods, which can be called the 'breaking-down methods' and on which we will say a few words.

These methods are static or dynamic. To study an organism statically it is necessary to begin by killing it. All descriptive sciences, such as anatomy, cytology, histology, embryology, compel the worker, at a given moment, to act like a curious child who breaks his toy so as to see the mechanism. Thanks to anatomy, we have acquired a perfect knowledge of the location and the shape of our organs, our muscles and the levers which they command, the bones. Anatomy, enlarging the field of its activity under the name of comparative anatomy, established enlightening analogies between living beings from the bottom to the top of the ladder. And not only between those living to-day, but between these and those which became extinct long ago. Anatomy is at the base of our knowledge of evolution in organized beings. It has rendered possible the notion of filiation of species and the issuance of a good many hypotheses which probably all contain a part of the truth, without one of them, it must be admitted, being able by itself to account for natural evolution.

The famous theories of Lamarck, Darwin, and de Vries have been the object of numerous critical works which are of great interest, and the reader is referred to the many books which exist on the subject.

Cytology, the science of cells, depends wholly on the use of the microscope as a tool of investigation, coupled together with selective dyes. The tissues are usually embedded in a block of paraffin wax which, when cool, maintains the fragile cellular elements so that they can be sliced in extremely thin layers, a thousandth of an inch thick. The entire sample of tissue having thus been cut into a considerable number of transparent pieces, it can readily be understood that the examination of a successive series enables the scientist to reconstitute exactly the architecture of the cell. The selective dyes are indispensable to show up the structural details which are otherwise invisible owing to the similarity of their refractive index, the absence of natural colour, and the thinness of the sections. Broadly, cytological and histological techniques consist in fixing, i.e. killing, the cells without deteriorating them and then colouring these sections by means of different substances (aniline dyes, for instance, or metallic impregnations).

We will not dwell on these methods which have rendered and continue to render great services. We will only point out that the purely morphological study of anatomical and cellular elements cannot furnish any information as to their physiological functions.

Dr. Alexis Carrel writes:[1]

'The structure of tissues and their functions are two aspects of the same thing. One cannot consider them separately. Each structural detail possesses its functional expression. It is through physiological aptitudes of their anatomical parts that the life of the higher animals is rendered possible. Likewise, the life of a community of ants depends on the physiological aptitudes of the individuals of which it is composed. When cells are considered only as structural elements, they are deprived of all the properties that make them capable of organizing as a living whole. Within the organism, they are associated according to certain laws. Cell sociology results from properties specific to each type of cell. Among these properties some manifest themselves under ordinary conditions of life, while others remain hidden. Tissues are endowed with potentialities far greater than those which are apparent. But these potentialities become actualized only when certain modifications of the internal environment occur, as, for instance, when pathogenic agencies are at work within the body. The

[1] A. Carrel, 'The New Cytology', *Science*, vol. 73, no. 1890, pp. 297–303 (1931).

significance of a given structural state is bound to the knowledge of the corresponding physiological state. Structure and function must be considered simultaneously.'

Furthermore, tissues evolve in time.

'A tissue consists of a society of complex organisms which does not respond in an instantaneous manner to the changes of the environment. It may oppose such changes for a long time before adapting itself to the new conditions through slight or profound transformations. To study it at only one instant of the duration is almost meaningless. The temporal extension of a tissue is as important as its spatial existence.'

The conception of cells and tissues which Carrel has substituted for the classical viewpoint is that of 'a system: cells-environment, of which the structural, functional, physical, physico-chemical and chemical conditions are considered in time as well as in space.' This constitutes a dynamic concept beside the purely static concept of the old cytology.

Physiology as a whole, one of the most fundamental sciences of life, of which almost all the others are but chapters, is essentially dynamic. Carrel's great merit has been to show that outside of a general physiology which considers complete organs preferably studied *in vivo*, a cellular physiology could be created which, without encroaching on the domain of general physiology, enables one to simplify the problems and to study the individual activities of each of the elements composing an organ. The name of 'breaking-down methods' which we employed in the beginning is thus justified. The method of tissue-culture outside of the organism enables one to go farther in the breaking-down process than does classical physiology. To make a rough comparison, the study of an automobile is divided into two stages. First, the study of the role and workings of the organs *in situ* and their breaking up as *complete* elements: dynamo, magneto, carburettor, motor, gears, etc. Second, the breaking up and analysis of the workings of each of these isolated elements. The knowledge of the whole is thus naturally enlarged. The comparison is, however, very superficial, inasmuch as the characteristic of Dr. Carrel's method consists in *maintaining the physiological activity* of the cellular elements, when they are detached from the organ. This renders possible a profound analysis of the mechanisms.

Fragments of tissue can be kept alive out of the organism. These fragments, preferably explanted[1] from an embryo, grow actively in an appropriate medium and possess the faculty of living indefinitely. The descendance of a small piece of chicken heart extracted from the egg in 1912 is still alive to-day after twenty-four years and shows no signs of ageing, that is to say that its growth-activity is the same as at the beginning. Barring ever-possible accidents—for the care it requires is considerable, and in spite of the precautions taken the cessation of its development can always be feared— there is no reason why it should ever die. It is superfluous to add that, had the chicken from which it was extracted lived its normal life, it would håve been dead long ago. Ten years constitutes about the extreme limit of duration of a chicken's existence. This method, on which we will have occasion to dwell in detail later on, presents tremendous advantages over the old cytology.

'The task of the new cytology,' says Carrel, 'is to discover the physiological properties which characterize each type of cell. It is impossible to attempt the study of these properties by any other method than that of pure cultures' (namely, constituted by a single type of cell). 'It is the only method which enables one to introduce precise modifications in the conditions of life of the colonies and to show up potentialities which often remain hidden during the normal

[1] *Explanted*, technical expression used in tissue-culture work, meaning 'removed from', 'cut off'. The term 'explant' is often used as a noun to define the fragment explanted.

life of a cell. Bacteriologists are not content to study the shape and the reactions of microbes in connexion with certain dyes, but also examine the aspect of their colonies, their action on the culture-medium, the poisons they secrete, their susceptibility to different antiseptics, the nutritive substances which they require, etc. The same is true of tissue-cells. Through our new techniques a cell type can be characterized by the appearance of its colonies, its mode of locomotion as recorded by cinematography, its effect on the coagulum, its rate of growth, the nature of the substances which inhibit cell-multiplication, the nature and concentration of the nutrient substances, etc.

'The new cytology permits the identification of cells and prediction of their conduct under given conditions. It reveals the specific properties of each type of cell. Thanks to it the mechanism of complex phenomena which take place in the normal or pathological tissues can be submitted to experimental analysis. Its fecundity will necessarily be greater than that of the classical cytology.'

The explanted tissues, kept alive, can be assimilated to ideal experimental animals. First, because they are simple and deprived of a nervous system; secondly, because they can be manufactured at will in large quantities. It is thus possible to experiment indefinitely on the same family of cells proceeding from the same stock. This eliminates innumerable causes of error due to the individual characteristics of animals of different origin. Furthermore, at each stage of an experiment, one disposes of a permanent control, since it is derived from the original culture itself, cut in two equal parts.

We have outlined a cursory view of certain methods which can be classed in the second category. We see that the unit is no longer the individual, but the cell, and that the principal tool of investigation is the microscope, as in the case of bacteriology. The limit of observation is what is called the *resolving power* of the microscope, that is to say the order of magnitude of the smallest objects which can be clearly distinguished by this instrument. It can easily be understood that it is useless to increase the magnification above a certain point if one loses in sharpness what is gained in dimensions. It is a fact of current observation for amateurs of photography, that there is nothing to be gained by enlarging the proofs beyond a certain size, which depends on the quality of the initial negative.

The preceding pages show that bacteriology is a science which belongs equally to both of the classes which we have examined, since microbes are at the same time individuals and isolated cells. But in fact, bacteriology studies cultures rather than microbes, and it is the entire culture which represents the individual rather than the microbes themselves.

CHAPTER II

PHYSICAL AND CHEMICAL METHODS— CRITICISMS AND DIFFICULTIES

WE now come to the third class of methods: chemical and physical methods. Let us listen once more to Claude Bernard.[1]

'The knowledge of the definite and elementary conditions of phenomena can only be attained in one way, namely by *experimental analysis*. Analysis dissociates all the complex phenomena successively into more and more simple phenomena, until they are reduced if possible to just two elementary conditions. Experimental science considers only the definite conditions which are necessary to produce a phenomenon. Physicists try to picture these conditions ideally, so to speak, in mechanics and mathematical physics. Chemists successively analyse complex matter, and in thus reaching either elements or definite substances (individual compounds or chemical species) they attain the elementary or irreducible conditions of phenomena. In the same way biologists should analyse complex organisms and reduce the phenomena of life to conditions that cannot be analysed in the present state of science. Experimental physiology and medicine have no other goal.'

All the functions of life are a remote consequence of the chemical functions of the molecules which enter into the constitution of each cell. Thus, one of the main problems of the modern biologist is the discovery of the relations existing between the structure and the properties of the elementary cellular substances, humours and tissues of a living organism, and the integral phenomenon which we call Life.

This affirmation admits an identity between the determinism

[1] *Introduction à l'étude de la médecine expérimentale*, 4th ed., 1920 (Delagrave), p. 113.

23

of the inorganized world and that of organized matter. There is much to be said, especially since the last few years, on the value of this determinism, for it has lost the character of absolute rigidity which was before attributed to it.

This question will be discussed more fully a little farther on. At any rate, the phenomena which enter into the field of our experimental studies are of an order of magnitude such that it can be admitted that everything occurs as if this determinism was absolute. In the same way, certain of our concepts were modified by the theory of relativity, but the description and quantitative examination of the objects of our experiments have not been *practically* affected. We again refer the reader to the *Introduction to the Study of Experimental Medicine* for the development of the reasons, hardly questioned to-day, which led to the adoption of this determinism.

Consequently, in first approximation, it can be said that all vital phenomena are dependent on the laws of energetics, and in particular, on the Carnot-Clausius law. They consequently contribute to the increase in entropy of the system of which living beings are a part, just as all the other phenomena resorting to chemistry and physics.

On the other hand, the majority of vital phenomena take place under conditions bordering on a state of equilibrium, which ordinarily leaves the choice between several different isodegradating paths. This second proposition puts in evidence the fact that living matter, in its evolution, obeys a law which *is not implicitly contained in the second principle of thermo-dynamics*. This important point has not escaped famous observers, for its trace is found in an article by Lord Kelvin, in another by von Helmholtz, in the works of Ch. E. Guye,[1] and of H. Freundlich.

If it is necessary to possess a thorough knowledge of the chemistry of living matter which alone can instruct the physiologist and the medical man as to the nature of the basic reactions of the phenomena which they are interested

[1] See Ch. E. Guye, *L'Evolution physico-chimique*, Chiron, Paris, 1922.

in, the experimenter must never forget that the living being forms a complete organism. It has a personality, and the biological phenomenon as a whole is not simply due to the summation of elementary chemical phenomena, but to the order in which these phenomena occur in time and space. This order appears to be the expression of a pre-determined purpose.

Sir Frederick Gowland Hopkins, one of the founders of modern bio-chemistry, wrote the following lines in 1925 (*Lancet*), in an article protesting against the term 'protoplasm' taken as a definition of the elementary living substance:

'There is no such thing as living matter in a specific sense. The special attribute of such systems from a chemical standpoint, is that these reactions are organized, and not that the molecules concerned are fundamentally different in kind from those the chemist meets elsewhere.'

The phenomena of life considered in their different aspects and intimate nature are thus simultaneously characterized by special forms which distinguish them as 'life phenomena' and by an identity of laws which incorporates them with the other phenomena of the cosmic world. It must be admitted that, if there are special procedures in all vital phenomena, at the same time they all obey the laws of mechanics, physics, and ordinary chemistry.

We have written, *it must*, purposely. This is not a profession of faith, for all professions of faith, be they vitalistic or materialistic, are unscientific. But it is important to orient research by means of a hypothesis, and it is impossible actually to avoid this one. That experiments should absolutely confirm or invalidate it, is immaterial to a man of science, or rather, to be exact, *should* be immaterial. Passions, which have nothing in common with science, have weighted the scales alternately on the vitalistic and mechanistic sides without any real benefit, for it is not by speeches but by experiments that human knowledge is advanced. There is much to be said on this subject, most of the discussions resting on misunder-standings. Religious questions, which are entirely separate, have been injected into these discussions and walls have been raised which prevent each party from observing what takes place at his neighbour's. Religion is a total stranger to these problems. It is necessary to be absolutely convinced of this in order to discuss them intelligently and fruitfully.

Descartes was a pure mechanist, and yet was a true believer. Claude Bernard, like most physiologists, admits a force, a vital impulse, but has no religious faith. From the point of view of pure method, Claude Bernard is more strictly Cartesian than Descartes. Ignorance of facts was at the base of Bichat's spiritualism, just as ignorance of facts is at the base of modern materialism. Every doctrine *a priori* other than the respect of the experimental fact is harmful and dangerous in science. The scientist should be a man of good faith before being a philosopher, a moralist, or even a citizen. Alas, should good faith be rarer than faith? It is useless to add that I have not only reference to religious but also to anti-religious faith. Although arising from a different source, the latter results in similar consequences and, in addition, kills hope.

To what degree can we actually accept the determinism which was the foundation of Claude Bernard's method?

'Life introduces absolutely no difference in the experi-mental scientific method which must be applied to the study of physiological phenomena, and in this respect the physio-logical sciences and the physico-chemical sciences depend on identically the same principles of investigation. In living as in inorganized matter the laws are immutable, and the phenomena which are governed by these laws are bound to their condition of existence by a necessary and absolute determinism.'

These lines, extracted from the *Introduction*, constitute a true act of faith or, if one prefers, a bold and very fruitful extrapolation; for it was evidently impossible in 1865 to affirm the necessary nature of an absolute determinism, based on undisputed experiments. It could certainly not be affirmed to-day. Yet the exact sciences have advanced since that period, and one of the clearest benefits which we have gained consists precisely in the new concept of determinism which has profoundly modified the significance of our experimental laws. To the physico-chemical law, which we had become accustomed to consider as fatal and ineluctable, a statistical law has been substituted, which, theoretically at least, admits very rare exceptions, *fluctuations* according to the consecrated term.[1] The absolute determinism of the physical and chemical laws is now replaced by a statistical determinism which is broader and more elastic, though practically as rigorous. Curiously enough, Claude Bernard's act of faith, admittedly based on an incomplete knowledge of phenomena, acquires in the light of the progress of mathematical physics a character of greater plausibility and generality. But contrary to what the great physiologist might have thought, it is not by proving the strictness of the determinism which he brandished as the emblem of his scientific philosophy, that the exact sciences have given a more probable value to his words. On the contrary, it is by opening the door to the possibility of very rare fluctuations practically escaping calculation. To study living organisms we are therefore obliged to depend on two postulates. We need not define the first, for we momentarily admit that it concerns the unknowable, the co-ordinated effort, the plan. The second, and only one which counts for us, establishes the identity of the laws governing inorganic and organized matter. The latter alone has the value of an indispensable working hypothesis.

Our ideas have become more flexible since the works of Gibbs and especially of Boltzmann. The 'determined' fact has become a 'probable' fact. The law of great numbers is at the base of all our physical laws. And now the old and

[1] For the development of these fundamental ideas, we again refer the reader to Ch. E. Guye's book *L'Evolution physico-chimique* (Chiron, Paris, 1922), an admirably clear account of one of the most significant and important advances of physico-chemistry.

already shaky determinism has had to undergo another assault, which, however, like the preceding one, has not practically changed its value as a tool.

Heisenberg, a brilliant mathematician, formulated in 1927 his 'Principle of Indeterminacy' which seriously modified our old ideas, for it introduced a certain degree of indetermination or imprevisibility of the future, as one of the fundamental postulates of the universe. This different point of view seems to transform the flow of time into a much more tangible phenomenon than it used to be in classical physics. *Every moment which passes introduces something new into the world which is not solely a mathematical extrapolation of all that existed previously.*[1] The classical determinism of Laplace which dominated science for so long stated that, if complete information concerning the entire state of the universe, the position and speed of each element of matter in space during the first minute of the year 1600, for example, could be obtained, it would be possible, by mere calculation, to deduct all the events of the past and of the future. The future is determined by the past, just as the solution of a differential equation is determined by the limiting conditions. Heisenberg demonstrated on the contrary, that only one half of the elements necessary to determine an event can be assembled (speed *or* position, but not both), as the other elements only come into existence *after* the accomplishment of the event. It is not ignorance, properly speaking, but a necessary limitation. It is the *principle of indetermination* which is now fully incorporated in modern physics. We can easily understand to what a degree this notion upsets the old ideas, even though

[1] There is in Bergson's *l'Evolution créatrice* a remarkable anticipation of the principle of indeterminacy: 'Thus our individuality develops, grows, and matures incessantly. Every moment adds something new to what was before. We will say more: not only new but unpredictable.' These lines were published in 1907, twenty years before Heisenberg.   In 1918 Franz Exner also emitted certain doubts as to the justification of determinism, and E. Schrödinger, who developed the ideas of Louis de Broglie, and like him was awarded the Nobel prize, was alone at that period in supporting Exner's ideas on 'the acausality of phenomena' (1922). See E. Schrödinger, *Science and the Human Temperament*, Norton & Co., New York, 1935.

a certain number of the most distinguished physicists refuse to subscribe to the logical philosophical consequences that can be deduced from it. They perhaps fear that the fragility of their theories will be shown up by the weakening of determinism. But this is tantamount to admitting that determinism is a dogma, and they quite rightly profess a violent dislike for dogmas in general. From our point of view, we simply wanted to mention this important theory which renders great services in undulatory mechanics, for it is sometimes good to be reminded that even exact sciences are far from having attained their definite form, assuming that such an expression is not entirely meaningless.

It is evident that this new concept is of a nature to upset the ideas of many people, especially of those, who unconsciously and as a result of a blind confidence in Science—with a capital S—had launched themselves into far-fetched extrapolations, of a purely speculative and unscientific nature. The combination of sentiment and science is not often a happy one, and I am inclined to think that certain optimistic anticipations, so flattering to the human mind, are nothing but a reaction against certain moral disciplines which all tend to glorify humility and severely condemn pride. At its dawn, science was greeted as a liberator. At that time the simplicity of a theory or a doctrine appeared as a proof of its value. New discoveries and events have taken it upon themselves to cure us of this candidness, which, however, has not yet quite disappeared from the world. But we are forced to admit to-day that science has not fulfilled the promises which man made in her name. We can only blame ourselves for this failure, as not a single experimental fact acquired in the past has ceased to be true. Science has never had to retract a single statement resulting from well-established facts within well-determined limits. The retractations that science has had to make were not of the domain of pure science, but concerned precisely the prediction of the future. Facts remain, but human anticipations fade away.

It is easy to discover the source of the fundamental error which led to hasty conclusions. The magnificent conquests of science induced us to believe that, by increasing indefinitely the precision of our measurements, we would be able to predict phenomena with ever-increasing accuracy. Unfortunately, experimental facts have proved that this hope was, and will always be, vain. It was found that the most capricious irregularities are observed when the precision of the measurement exceeds a certain point and enables one to penetrate into the realm of the up till now inaccessible small elements, the postive and negative electron, the photon. No refinement of techniques can enable us to predict the movements of these corpuscles which seem to be determined by the most disordered fantasy. We must repeat that, from a practical point of view, this state of things not only in no way disturbs the evolution of inorganic phenomena nor what we call the principle of causality, but also that this disorder is the *necessary* condition of our physical laws. These are only rigorous on condition that the movements of the elementary particles are absolutely disorderly, and if they ceased to be so, the laws would cease to be valid. For, as we said above, the laws of great numbers, of probability, enter into play. All our phenomena are but 'envelope' phenomena, and the result, at our scale, of an immense number of elementary phenomena which escape observation. They are statistical laws. There is therefore only one thing changed: our old notion of determinism, our ideas on the *real* significance of the relation of cause to effect. But the possible occurrence, under certain conditions, of fluctuations which occasionally transpose the 'fantasy' of the elementary corpuscles to a higher scale, still not directly observable, but capable of influencing vital phenomena, limits in a certain measure our power of prediction, that is to say our science.[1]

[1] The development of these concepts would exceed the scope of this book. Nevertheless we think we ought to insist on the fact that these limitations only concern the individual elementary particles and *not* the current objects of our science. These, as well as all the phenomena which we study, consist of, or bring into play, such a

Let us take an example. If heredity depended on the play of a considerable number of identical elements, there would be no problem. The laws of chance would apply, excluding all sudden mutations, or rather rendering them improbable. The apparition of mutations seems to show on the contrary that we are in the presence of too feeble a number of elements. It is an analogous case to that of tiny communicating vases containing a few molecules of gas. The displacement of one single molecule destroys the statistical result. Boyle's law no longer applies. The second law of thermo-dynamics is upset. So that the real and greatest intellectual problem of man, which covers all the problems of life, can actually be reduced to a very simple question: How is order born of disorder? By 'order' we mean the natural sequence of perceptible phenomena.

·   ·   ·   ·   ·

Let us now leave this somewhat hallucinating realm, admirably evoked in the last chapter of Sir James Jeans' *The Mysterious Universe*, where all reality is reduced to groups

tremendous number of particles that the action of one isolated elementary particle has absolutely no value with respect to the phenomenon as a whole. It is in this sense that we said that *practically* there was nothing changed. We are incapable of predicting the future of *one* particle, but there are so many of them that the calculation of probabilities enables us to establish with a very great degree of approximation the probable *statistical* result of the sum of their individual actions (kinetic theory of gases, for example) as revealed by experiments. In the same way an insurance company is incapable of predicting *which* of the insured houses will be burned or *which* client will die. The only thing which interests it is the annual percentage of each disaster, percentage which is calculated from the statistics of the preceding years. It is thus possible with a small sum to cover the risks representing a much larger amount. This enables one to understand how chance can give birth to precise laws, and one comprehends also why it is necessary that chance alone should determine the fate of each individual, for if a new element enters into play—for instance a world-wide cataclysm (epidemic, earthquake)—which superimposes itself on normal chances of individual accidents, the law of statistics no longer applies and the company fails. That is the so-called 'fluctuation'.

of equations, and return to the chemical bases of vital functions. We shall see that other difficulties await us.

The analysis of elements constituting living matter or elaborated by it, rapidly demonstrated that it was composed of elementary substances in no way different from those found everywhere in nature. The carbon of coal and diamond, the potassium, sodium, and calcium of inorganic salts, the nitrogen and oxygen of air are identical with those of our tissues or of our blood. There was therefore, in principle, no reason why the classical methods of chemistry should not be applicable to the basic substances of organized matter. In analysing these compounds the conviction was rapidly obtained that a great number of simple elements entered into their constitution. In the same way any machine or any work of art can be reduced under the mortar to a given quantity of chemical bodies and definite elements. But a machine, a work of art, a living organism, only exist as such by reason of an *organization* at a scale superior to that of molecular magnitude. At this scale, the properties of the constituent molecules seem to efface themselves in order to allow the birth of new properties due to their conjunction in space and in time, in definite proportions, following an order, a plan which establishes a bond between them, and which creates their reason of existence and their harmony.[1] This brings us back to Hopkins' observation, quoted on page 25.

In brief, our body is made up of cells, the cells of molecules, and the molecules of atoms. But these atoms are not *all* the reality of the human body. The way in which the atoms, the molecules, and the cells are arranged, and which results in the unity of the individual, is also a reality, and how much more interesting. The molecules of any substance can always be decomposed into their atomic elements, and these in turn into their sub-atomic elements, the electrons and the protons. But this dissociation results in the disappearance of the properties which gave this molecule its chemical individuality

[1] In connexion with harmony in science, the first pages of Henri Poincaré's admirable book, *Science et Méthode*, should be read.

PART II

CICATRIZATION OF WOUNDS AND TISSUE-CULTURE

CHAPTER IV

A BIOLOGICAL PHENOMENON—THE CICATRIZATION OF WOUNDS—TIME— PRELIMINARY EXPERIMENTS

WE will now examine in detail a phenomenon which is familiar to everybody. Cicatrization can be studied either *in vivo* or *in vitro* and therefore belongs to the methods of Class B.

This phenomenon is too complex to lend itself to chemical analysis as a whole. It is a manifestation of the cellular activity of reparation and proliferation. We propose to show the reader how the quantitative laws were established, by making him successively participate in all the stages of the experiments and in the reasoning which led to their discovery.

But before delving into the heart of the subject, we would like to change the tone adopted in the preceding chapters, for the following reasons.

Up till now we have spoken of general questions. We have exposed the different points of view of eminent scientists, living or dead, and we have expressed our own opinion. In conformance to an old habit, we have avoided speaking in the first person as is done in original papers. This is a convention, which is not followed by everybody and which misleads no one. The aim pursued by the author in all scientific papers is to efface his personality as much as possible and to let the facts speak for themselves. This, at any rate, is the end that everybody should seek and that most of us attain, even when 'I' is employed instead of 'we'.

One of the principal tasks of the experimenter is the elimination of the 'individual factor' or 'personal coefficient'. There are always too many causes of error, and this particular one can take on different aspects. The observers are not identically sensitive to light radiations, to sound. The way in which they appreciate the equality of two juxtaposed

coloured areas is not quite similar. Their movements are
more or less rapid, more or less precise. Their reactions
more or less slow. At different moments of the day, the same
person does not always react in the same fashion to the same
stimulus. Hence the necessity of resorting as often as possible
to automatic or recording instruments. It can be admitted
that one of the reasons for employing the pronoun 'we' has
the same origin. It imposes a more neutral redaction than the
'I'. Another reason lies in the fact that several workers have
often materially collaborated in different ways to the discovery of the experimental facts described in a paper. Still
other motives may exist.

The result of these combined considerations is that the
perusal of a totally impersonal scientific article, from which
all human element has been systematically eliminated, is
impossible for all but a student of the same subject or one
directly connected with it, and who is interested enough to
seek only facts and measurements in the text. In other words,
only a specialist reads it.

And yet there is something else in a discovery or a scientific
endeavour. First, the human element which has been carefully put aside, and second, all the intermediary steps between
the salient points of the reasoning, the stages which establish
the continuity, the homogeneity of the psychological evolution
which enabled the worker to reach his anticipated goal. Only
these elements could make the paper interesting to a non-
specialized reader. An article written in this fashion would
be too long and encumbered by useless details as far as the
scientist is concerned, but not without interest from the
point of view of the 'story' of a discovery. To be complete,
the description of researches having attained a definite result
would require the mention of a great number of facts the use-
fulness of which vanishes when the final end is achieved, but
which, at a certain moment, have served as cement, or as a
link between more important facts. The elimination of these
links leaves, instead of a continuous curve, a series of points,
the interrelationship of which is not sufficiently clear to allow

an outsider to understand their logical sequence. Such a reader will gladly skip a table of figures, but if the work is in itself new and original he will perhaps be interested in the mechanism of the development of the ideas, hypotheses, experiments, and results of the author. In other words he would be interested in the *manner* in which the results have been obtained as much as in the results themselves.

This point of view is quite different from that of vulgarization. The vulgarizer translates articles and books which are written in a conventional jargon meant to economize thought and time, into a language which is accessible to the unspecialized public. He eliminates mathematics which are nothing else but a condensed form of mental stenography. But he does not introduce the more interesting human touch, or if he does so, it is because a particular phase of the work in question presents a specially picturesque, striking, or amusing aspect. He does not try to extricate the general line, the slim psychological thread which binds together the successive stages of the evolution of a discovery in the brain of a scientist. Yet it is the *romance* of a discovery which could seemingly be capable of fixing the attention of the layman. This novel, once lived, is destroyed. Only the material conclusions of each chapter are allowed to subsist.

It is true that the vulgarizer or commentator would find it very difficult to reassemble the pieces of the puzzle furnished by scientific papers, so as to be able to unite these elements in the logical and harmonious order which led to their birth. It would be quite impossible for him to divulge the succession of psychological facts of which they are the fruit, had he not assisted in person at all the different phases of the work or had the author not taken him into his intimate confidence. A few such examples, however, exist. The most celebrated is certainly the admirable *Life of Pasteur* by René Vallery-Radot. The realization of this monumental and profoundly moving fresco is due to the family bond existing between the genial scientist and the author.

In English-speaking countries, however, didactic works are

sometimes and even quite often found, the extreme dryness of which is attenuated by portraits, short biographies, and reproductions of old engravings, historically connected with the text. Bayliss' remarkable *Principles of General Physiology*, for example, is a living and fascinating book, full of pictures which relax the mind of the student. In America, excellent text-books such as *Practical Physiological Chemistry*, by Hawk and Bergeim, and *Applied Chemistry*, by Morse, are illustrated with portraits of the scientists whose works are cited.

But there is no attempt to expose the mechanism, the genesis of a work, the interest of which, if it exists, can be quite independent of the value of the effort or of the result. I will, therefore, in the following pages, report my experiments and results published in the *Journal of Experimental Medicine*, without eliminating the intermediary stages of my researches. The reader will thus be able to follow the evolution of the work in my mind and the succession of ideas and reasoning. I will not vulgarize nor simplify, I will develop instead of shortening, and will reintroduce in part the personal element which had been smothered and hidden. The reader must excuse me if the subject is mediocre; my choice is necessarily limited to my own experiments, and this restriction reduces its interest.

.   .   .   .   .

Towards the end of 1914 I found myself at Compiègne as Lieutenant commanding Section R.V.F. B. 26, in charge of victualling the 61st Reserve Division. At the same period, Dr. Carrel was transforming the Hôtel du Rond Royal into Front Hospital no. 21. This hospital was destined to become a centre of research, for people were beginning to realize that it might be useful to be able to recommend officially certain methods for the treatment of infected wounds and that a selection amongst those employed was necessary. Professional surgeons adapted themselves rapidly to circumstances, and owing to their experience and their knowledge inspired no fears. This was not the case, however, with the general practitioners who had been obliged to transform themselves instantaneously into surgeons, and who often found themselves brutally faced with important lesions for the immediate treatment of which they possessed scant information, and no training.

The expenses of the laboratories of Temporary Hospital 21 were supported by the Rockefeller Institute of New York.

Dr. Carrel asked me one day what method could be employed for measuring exactly the surface of any kind of a plane area. In fact, he was interested in estimating the surface of wounds which he was studying with Dr. Alice Hartmann, and which were outlined on cellophane by means of a wax pencil or even a fountain pen. He told me that up till then he had employed the weighing method, which consists in transferring the first drawing obtained directly on the wound on to a sheet of paper, which is then cut out following the lines of the drawing as exactly as possible, and weighed.

Figures proportional to the areas of the wounds are thus obtained on condition that the paper utilized is always of the same thickness. He explained the inconveniences of this technique, which was delicate, lengthy, and inaccurate. I suggested employing the planimeter, an instrument well known to engineers, which enables one to evaluate in a few minutes, with precision, the area of any surface in square centimetres. The problem which was occupying Dr. Carrel at the time was the following one. He had been able to convince himself that the cicatrization of surface wounds maintained under proper conditions evolves according to a geometric law. This phenomenon had not been studied quantitatively, owing to the fact that its only interest before the war was a purely physiological one. Furthermore, in order to solve it, some notion of mathematics was necessary and, at that time, mathematical culture was not generally found amongst biologists. Carrel thought that I might succeed and asked me to study the question. He believed that the solution would solve rapidly and without possible discussion, the question of the relative value of the different treatments proposed for the dressing of wounds and that of the influence of certain retarding or accelerating factors.

He had already made some beautiful experiments on cicatrization, that marvellous phenomenon which begins as soon as our skin or our muscles or our tendons are wounded, and stops when the lesion is repaired. In a cut, a burn, a torn tissue, all the cells concerned, asleep so to speak until then, wake up and multiply with feverish activity, reproduce by millions, repair the damage as well as possible, and then fall back into their latent life. We are no longer surprised by this admirable labour because we have seen it since childhood. Familiarity kills wonder.

'The cicatrization and regeneration of tissues are the manifestations of the tendency to persist which is inherent to all living organisms. We are profoundly ignorant of the nature of these phenomena. They are, like the function of nutrition, a fundamental property of living matter. It is as impossible to know their essence as it is to know the essence of life. Moreover, this knowledge would be useless. From a metaphysical point of view, it might be interesting to know why a wound cicatrizes. But from a scientific point of view, it is infinitely more important to know *how* it cicatrizes. It would thus become possible to determine the efficient causes of the complex mechanism of the regeneration of tissues. That is why it is useful to study the physiological phenomena of cicatrization. It is true that the regenerating power escapes our methods of research, but the physico-chemical processes which are co-ordinated and harmonized by this directing force in view of the morphological reparation can enter into our field of experiment.'

It was in 1908 that Dr. Carrel wrote these lines which he later communicated to me and with which I began my Thesis in 1917. At the same time, he gave me the unpublished results of his experiments. I will summarize them here so that the reader may have all the elements which I myself possessed at the beginning of my work in 1915.

Carrel's experiments represent the first systematic study of these phenomena. They led him to the culture of tissues *in vitro*, and this second problem caused him to abandon the first. The work was accomplished at the Rockefeller Institute in New York, and principally on dogs. The wounds were obtained by resecting a piece of skin of geometrical, i.e. rectangular, trapezoidal, or circular, shape. To distinguish the edge of the original wound he preferably employed dogs with a black skin, or else tattooed the outline of the wound on the epidermis with India ink. It was thus easy to follow the evolution of the phenomenon of cicatrization. The dressing consisted in an application of sterile talcum or of hot paraffin wax. The wounds were kept as sterile as possible. It is superfluous to add that all operations were made under complete anaesthesia.

Under these conditions the following facts were brought forth. Cicatrization passes through four phases or periods.

1. *Quiescent or latent period.* This is the period which stretches between the moment of the resection and that when *granular contraction* sets in. *Granulations* are small protuberances resembling somewhat a cauliflower, but of a bright red colour. They are generally dry, shiny, and of a healthy aspect on a sterile wound. During these first days the dimensions of the wound do not change. Hence the name given to this period, the duration of which is variable in different wounds (one to five days). At the end of that time, the period of contraction suddenly starts. (Fig. 1.)

2. *Period of granular contraction.* At this moment the edges of the wound begin to come closer together. Very quickly at first, then slower. The rate of this contraction depends on the surface of the wound and not on its age, as was believed until then. In order to demonstrate this clearly, Carrel cut out two rectangular wounds of different sizes on the same dog. The large sides measured respectively 66 and 26 millimetres. In the course of the first 48 hours the length of the larger one

(these experiments were made before the use of the planimeter) decreased by 20 millimetres (a little less than one third),
whereas the length of the small one decreased by only 4
millimetres, about one sixth.

For the same reason, when the wounds were of trapezoidal

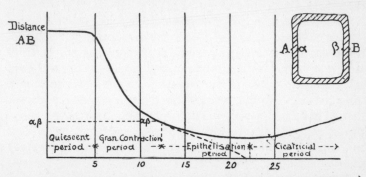

FIG. I. (EXPERIMENTAL WOUND IN THE UPPER RIGHT-HAND CORNER.)
POINTS A AND B ARE ON THE OUTLINE TATTOOED WITH INDIA INK.
POINTS α AND β ARE ON THE NEWLY FORMED EPITHELIAL BORDER. THE
SCHEMATIC CURVE SHOWS THE SUCCESSIVE PHASES OF CICATRIZATION.
ORDINATES EXPRESS THE DISTANCE BETWEEN POINTS A AND B (SOLID
CURVE) AND α AND β (DOTTED CURVE) AS A FUNCTION OF TIME

shape, the length of the longer base tended to equalize itself
with that of the smaller one and the wounds became rectangular in a few days. The same results were obtained with
circular wounds made by punching out the skin. It was then
established that the rate of reparation during the granular
period was a function of the dimension of the wound, that is
to say, of the total effort required to repair the destroyed area.

This law had already been established by Spallanzani for
salamanders.[1] It was thus proved to be equally true for
mammals. This was unforeseen considering the differences
of the mechanisms brought into play. Minervini, in 1904,[2]
had found the same phenomena. However, as he made no
measurements, he did not conceive the existence of the curve

[1] Spallanzani, *Experiences pour servir à l'histoire de la génération des
animaux et des plantes* (1787).
[2] Minervini, *Virchows Ann.*, vol. 175, p. 238 (1904).

represented on Fig. 1. The different processes of cicatrization had not escaped him, but he thought it impossible to
succeed in formulating a law sufficiently general to cover them
all. He therefore abandoned the problem to devote himself
exclusively to the histological side of the question, which also
attracted a certain number of other workers.

This period of contraction during which the surface of the
wound decreases solely by means of a movement of the underlying tissue, plays an important part in the cicatrization of
large and medium-sized wounds and especially of the latter,
at any rate on dogs. When studying the rate of reparation of
different-sized wounds on these animals, it becomes apparent
that wounds which are too large do not cicatrize as quickly as
the others. It might almost be said that everything takes place
as though the activity of reparation was maximum for wounds
that dogs are likely to inflict on each other.

Strange to say, it seems that the phenomenon of contraction
is closely dependent on the presence of the granulations. It
does not exist before their apparition (latent period) and it
stops when the epidermization is complete, that is when the
granulations have been covered by a thin layer of epithelial
cells, foundation of the new skin, which slowly invades the
wound from the edges. In order to ascertain whether these
phenomena were bound together by a relation of causality,
Carrel made the following experiment.

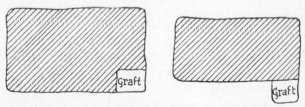

FIGS. 2 AND 3. EFFECT OF A GRAFT ON THE GRANULAR
CONTRACTION

He grafted a small piece of skin in the corner of a rectangular
wound covered with granulations. A deformation took place,
but at the end of a few days, the wound had reassumed its

rectangular aspect (Figs. 2 and 3). 'This proves that contraction stopped at the level of the graft while it continued to act everywhere else.'

In another experiment, he stimulated the epithelization of a large square wound which showed no trace of epithelium in the lower part by grafting a small piece of epithelium. It is a well-established fact that a living graft increases the production of epithelial cells. It was then observed (Figs. 4, 5, and 6) that the distance between the lines tattooed in India

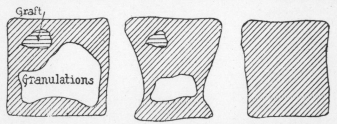

FIGS. 4, 5, AND 6. EFFECT OF A GRAFT ON THE GRANULAR CONTRACTION

ink on the edges of the wound, decreased in the lower part (presence of granulations) while it remained constant in the upper part (absence of granulations). The wound became trapezoidal (Fig. 5) and when totally healed resumed its primitive shape. It is therefore certain that epithelization inhibits the function of contraction of the granulations. When epithelization is precocious, the scar is large and thin. When it is slow, the contraction is stronger and the scar is thick and comparatively smaller.

The preparation of the surface of the wound for the migration of the epithelial cells is also a function of the granulations. But it seems that their principal role is to bring the edges of the wound within a certain distance of each other, about 10 or 15 millimetres in a dog. This may be deduced from the fact that a wound which is 10 millimetres broad, no longer contracts. The contraction becomes useless because at a distance of 10 millimetres the secondary mechanism, namely epithelization, functions easily, as we will show farther on.

A beautiful experiment of Carrel's proves that an external excitation is necessary to set the process of reparation going. A fresh and sterile wound, carefully covered by a sheet of cellophane glued to the skin and therefore completely protected against any external action, does not cover itself with granulations and does not cicatrize. In other words, the skin, which is a protective element, has no reason to reappear, and therefore does not reconstitute itself.

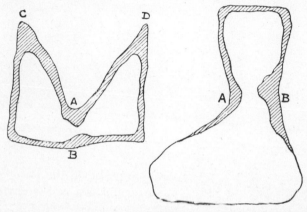

FIGS. 7 AND 8. AT A AND B THE DISTANCE BETWEEN THE EPITHELIAL BORDERS BEING SMALLER (LESS THAN 15 MILLIMETRES), EPITHELIZATION IS MARKEDLY FASTER, AS WELL AS IN THE ANGLES C AND D

3. *Period of Epithelization or Epidermization.* The beginning of the epithelization period can easily be observed on a rectangular wound which has been outlined with India ink. The new epithelium, which later becomes the scar, progresses at first very slowly at the surface of the granulations. It is extremely thin and fragile, and there are numerous factors which hinder its development. (The experiments subsequently realized at the Compiègne Hospital showed that the most important of them was infection). The observation of trapezoidal wounds shows the rapidity of cellular proliferation (epidermization) at the smaller base in comparison with its slowness at the longer base. In wounds of

irregular shape, epithelization always begins at the sharp angles where the distance between the edges of the wound is smaller (Figs. 7 and 8). The new cells seem to attract one another. Though the intimate mechanism of this phenomenon escapes us, it explains the acceleration of cicatrization by grafts. Carrel made the following experiment in order to demonstrate this particular point. Fig. 9 shows a rectangular

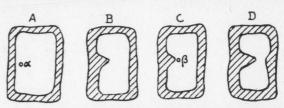

FIG. 9. EFFECT OF A GRAFT ON EPITHELIZATION

wound in which epidermization has begun (A). A tiny epithelial graft, less than 1 millimetre square, and taken from the new epithelium just being formed, is disposed at point α. A few days later the wound appears as in Fig. B. The small graft has been rejoined and absorbed by the neighbouring epithelium. A new graft was placed in the same manner in front of the peninsula formed at β (C). Fig. D shows that not only has the epithelial peninsula surrounded the new graft but that the attraction due to the coming together of the two edges can be observed on the opposite border of the wound.[1]

The cellular reparation activity, the epidermization, is therefore all the greater, the nearer the edges of the wound are to each other. Whereas the granular contraction acts when they are farther apart. When examined through the microscope, the granulations assume the aspect of a relief map, showing ranges of rounded hills separated by valleys at the bottom of which a certain serosity can be detected. The epithelial cells, either isolated or in groups, travel on the surface of this liquid. Their reunion at the point where several

[1] Reverdin had already signalled a similar phenomenon.

valleys converge gives birth to islets. These islets are called spontaneous grafts.

When part of a cicatrizing wound is covered by a sheet of sterile filter paper, it can be observed that epithelization progresses more rapidly where the cells have been protected by the sheet of paper. This experiment is not in contradiction

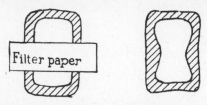

FIG. 10.   INFLUENCE OF MECHANICAL PROTECTION
ON EPITHELIZATION

with the complete inhibition due to the application of cellophane over the entire wound mentioned above.   In the first case, the period of contraction had not begun and the cellophane was impermeable, whereas in the second, the period of epidermization has already started and filter paper is not impermeable.   It acts only as a local protection.   (Fig. 10.)

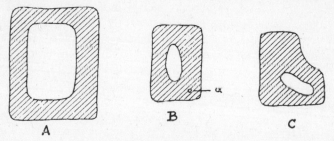

FIG. 11.   INFLUENCE OF INFECTION

On the other hand, the following experiment shows the retarding action of infection (Fig. 11). A wound was cicatrizing normally. When it had attained the dimensions of B, Fig. 11, it was observed that there was a point of infection in a corner of the new epithelial tissue at α. The wound was not sterilized. A few days later, it assumed the aspect shown in C, Fig. 11.

The presence of the small centre of infection had sufficed to bring the lower edge of the wound almost back to its original dimension.

4. *Cicatricial Period.* The scar left by a large wound is proportionally smaller than that left by a small wound. A wound 66 millimetres long left a scar of 22 millimetres, whilst a wound 26 millimetres long, on the same animal, left a scar of 13 millimetres. In the first case the scar represents one third, and in the second case, one half of the size of the original wound. In small wounds of about 10 millimetres, the scar is almost as extensive as the wound. When the epidermization is ended and the wound healed, the scar begins to spread and distends itself (see Fig. 1) so that points A and B tend to come back to their original position. This last period is very long (several months) and completes the regeneration of the lesion.

In brief, the mechanisms of the phenomenon of cicatrization are co-ordinated in such a fashion that the reparation is continuous. For dogs, the processes are adapted to the quick healing of small and medium-sized wounds, not wider than 40 millimetres. In a wound 30 to 40 millimetres wide the contraction is very efficient, and in a short while the edges are brought to within 10 or 15 millimetres of each other, a distance which is favourable to epidermization. Thus, at the moment when the rate of reparation through contraction tends to slow up, epithelization starts in and the work of regeneration continues without interruption, but by means of a different mechanism.

I have dwelt at length on these preliminary experiments because it was necessary for the reader to know the subject and to be familiar with the terminology. What precedes suffices to explain the complexity of the phenomenon which had to be translated quantitatively by the simplest possible formula. The problem which I had to solve was perfectly well defined. It consisted in finding a method which would permit us to predict in advance the dimension of any kind of wound at the end of 4, 8, 15, . . ., x days and, consequently, to calculate how many days the wound would require to be completely healed. The part of different retarding agents had to be appreciated, and either the real factors which govern the phenomenon discovered, or, more likely, the efficient and measurable factors which, under an apparent simplicity dissimulate an infinite number of inaccessible active elements.

This goal once attained, it would be possible to determine mathematically, instead of empirically as heretofore, the advantages and inconveniences of the different methods proposed for the treatment of wounds, the effect of different antiseptics and their respective qualities. A motivated choice could thus be made and cicatrization obtained in as brief a time as possible.

Was the problem soluble? Would not each case obey its own particular laws, or rather be rendered independent of general laws and mathematics by imponderable factors such as the individual temperament of each invalid, his heredity, his former life, his habits, the suffering which he had gone through in the war? This was what I had to find out.

CHAPTER V

CICATRIZATION OF WOUNDS (II)— EXPERIMENTAL TECHNIQUE—CURVES— MATHEMATICAL STUDY

IT was first of all necessary to establish a precise technique whereby wounds could be maintained sterile without irritation, and the edges outlined as accurately as possible. Dr. H. D. Dakin had already prepared a certain number of antiseptics and Dr. Carrel had chosen the ones which bore the numbers 30 and 142 as giving the best practical results. '30', as we called it, was the sodium hypochlorite solution which later became famous under the name of Dakin Solution.

This slightly alkaline antiseptic, rigorously titrated at 0·5 per cent of sodium hypochlorite, differs radically from other hypochlorite solutions used for cleaning purposes (Javel water). These latter fluids are very irritating and can determine grave lesions of the tissues on account of their high percentage of free alkali. Their antiseptic power, however, is not due to their alkalinity; that is to say, to their causticity. The Dakin solution possesses a strong antiseptic power without being irritating or toxic, and this constitutes a tremendous advantage.

It was furthermore necessary to avoid as much as possible all disturbing influences on the wounds and, in particular, to make sure, by daily checks, that their bacterial condition, viz. the mean number of microbes per unit of surface, was minimum and did not vary from the beginning to the end of the experiment.

The patients had to lie in bed, preferably immobilized by a fracture, for example, as any movement always brings about considerable delay in cicatrization.

The bacterial condition of the wound was therefore controlled every day by smears taken from different points and examined under the microscope. If microbes were found, they were destroyed by appropriate treatment. The granulated surface and environing skin were carefully washed with neutral sodium oleate (soap). The granulations were then sterilized by means of the Dakin solution (no. 30)[1] or no. 142 (sodium toluene—sulphonchloramide, Dakin), for short: Chloramine-T. When the microscopic examination showed that sterilization had been obtained, the wound was dressed either with neutral sodium stearate containing small quantities of antiseptic, or simply with vaseline, lanoline, or salt water (physiological isotonic solution at 0·9 per cent of sodium chloride). It was thus possible to maintain wounds bacteriologically sterile during several weeks, sometimes months. The daily bacterial examination immediately revealed any return of infection and permitted us to take it into account in the interpretation of the experiment. It was on wounds thus prepared according to Dr. Carrel's technique that the progress of cicatrization was studied as well as the comparative action of different antiseptics.

As I have already explained, the drawing of the wound was obtained by means of cellophane. These thin sterile sheets were applied on the surface of the wound with a dab of cotton. The outline of the epithelial edge or outline of the granulations was drawn with a dermographic or wax pencil, and also when possible the edge of the cicatrix at the line of junction with the healthy skin. This drawing was then reproduced on a sheet of ordinary paper. Fig. 12 is the reproduction of such a series of drawings from the beginning (moment when the wound was recognized as sterile) to the end of the experiment. As can be seen, the drawings were generally made every four days. The area of each drawing could then be obtained in square centimetres by means of the planimeter. When the outline of the cicatrix could be taken, a second figure was obtained.

The graphic expression of the curve was easy to establish. As is customary, the time was carried as abscissae, that is to say horizontally on millimetre paper (squared in millimetres)

[1] Later prepared according to Dr. Daufresne's improved technique.

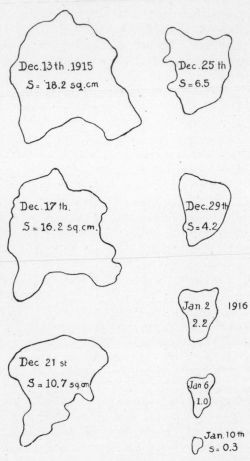

Patient No 221

Dec. 13th 1915
S = 18.2 sq. cm

Dec. 25th
S = 6.5

Dec. 17th.
S = 16.2 sq. cm.

Dec. 29th
S = 4.2

Jan. 2   1916
2.2

Dec 21 st
S = 10.7 sq. cm

Jan 6
1.0

Jan. 10th
S = 0.3

FIG. 12. REDUCED REPRODUCTION OF THE DRAW-
INGS OF A WOUND, TAKEN FOUR DAYS APART.
THESE DRAWINGS REPRESENT THE OUTLINE OF
THE GRANULATIONS, LIMITED BY THE NEW
EPITHELIAL BORDER. (SEE FIG. 13.)

and the surfaces vertically as ordinates. To every day corresponded a given area. If the measurements were made every four days, a curve similar to that of Fig. 13, which represents the evolution of the wounds of Fig. 12, was obtained. Once in possession of a certain number of similar curves, I could begin to work, rocked day and night by the unceasing

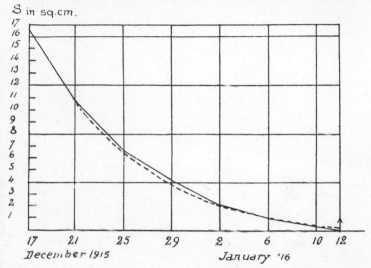

FIG. 13. NORMAL HEALING OF A WOUND. THE DISCREPANCIES BETWEEN THE TWO CURVES— OBSERVED (SOLID CURVE) AND CALCULATED (DOTTED CURVE)— ARE SMALL. THE MAXIMUM DIFFERENCE AMOUNTS TO 0·6 SQ. CM. ON THE 29TH OF JANUARY

bombardment which formed a sonorous background to all our thoughts and all our actions. I intended to begin by attacking the surface and then the length of the epithelial edge. The first idea was to express the quantity cicatrized in one day *as a function of the dimension of the wound.* For if I expressed in square centimetres the area cicatrized in a time t, I failed to take into account the fact that a large wound can, in an equal time, cicatrize a surface which is larger in absolute values, but which may be smaller in relative value, namely, with respect to its total area.

In other words, if the wound no. 221 (Fig. 12) has shrunk by 5·5 square centimetres in four days, between the 17th and 21st of December, and if another wound no. 263 has diminished by 20 square centimetres (from 110 to 90 cm.^{2}) it is not certain that it is the first one which has been the slower to cicatrize. In the first case, the initial surface was 16.2 cm.^{2} (previous to that it was infected); 5·5 cm.^{2} therefore represents about one third of the total area of the wound; whereas, in the case of no. 263, 20 square centimetres correspond to one fifth of the area. It is the smaller one, therefore, which healed quicker.

As a consequence it was quite natural to express the quantity cicatrized as a fraction of the work accomplished *with respect to the total work to be accomplished*, that is to say, in relative units. To do this it sufficed to divide the area cicatrized in a given time, by the total area at the beginning of the experiment. S being the initial surface at the moment when infection, one of the principal causes of delay, has been eliminated, and S' the surface at the end of a time t (expressed in days), the work accomplished with respect to the total surface S will be:

$$\frac{S-S'}{S} \quad\dots\dots\dots\dots\dots\dots\dots\dots \text{(1)}$$

In the examples cited, the value of this ratio is 5·5 : 16·2 = 0·34 for the first and 20 : 110 = 0·18 for the second, in round figures. Experience soon showed that a small wound will, in all cases, heal relatively quicker than a large one. The surface of the wound seemed thus to play a primary part.

On the other hand, it was necessary to introduce time into our formula in order to express the quantity cicatrized per day. This was done by dividing the quotient $\dfrac{S-S'}{S}$ by t, number of days elapsed between the measurement of the area S and the measurement of area S', just as one divides the number of miles by the time, to obtain the mean velocity of a distance travelled. The formula became then:

$$\frac{\dfrac{S-S'}{S}}{t}, \text{ or: } \frac{S-S'}{S \times t} \dotfill (2)$$

I was thus in possession of a simple element of calculation which expressed the quantity cicatrized per day between the two measurements as a function of the total area of the wound in question. One of two things must happen. Either the wound would continue to cicatrize at the same rate, or else other factors would intervene, and influence the velocity of repair in proportion as the wound diminished. It was hardly probable that the first hypothesis would be verified, for it was too simple. Hence, there were few chances that my first formula could be applied to the following period. In fact, I observed a certain progressive divergence. It now behoved me to study this discrepancy and to find a new factor the variations of which would remain proportional to it. This factor introduced into the formula would give it a constant value from the beginning to the end of the phenomenon. In case of success, the problem was solved, for it would then be possible to calculate the curve from point to point.

The difference between the biological method of approach and the mathematical method borrowed from the physical sciences is here clearly shown. The preceding chapter gave the reader an idea of the multiplicity of the factors and of the complexity of the problem. The solution had not yet been found, because those who had studied it were too familiar with the details of the phenomenon. Knowing a great many physiological factors but ignoring their relative influence, they did not dare eliminate them, and did not know how to take them into account. They were paralysed by their knowledge.

Like the botanist who could not see the forest because of the trees, they could only consider the facts as a function of microscopic biological elements with which they were familiar. My ignorance of these elements freed me from the chains which fettered them. Not knowing how to distinguish the different species, I examined the forest from a distance, as a whole and quantitatively as I had been taught to do for a physical phenomenon. Dr. Carrel had foreseen that a brain trained in such methods was better adapted to attack this problem than one inhibited by a mass of knowledge and by habits of thought.

The problem was then momentarily reduced to finding a way of obtaining a constant value for this formula by introducing a 'new measurable element, varying in the same manner as the differences observed between the experimental values and those calculated from the formula.

First of all, of what order of magnitude were the discrepancies, and what was the law of their variation?

Let us go back to wound no. 221. We have seen that the cicatrized area was 5·5 square centimetres between the first and fourth day; this gave the following values for formula (2) ($S=16\cdot2$; $S'=10\cdot7$)

$$\frac{S-S'}{S\times t} = \frac{5\cdot5}{16\cdot2\times4} = 0\cdot085 \text{ (in round figures)}.$$

For the second period of four days, we find:

$S'=10\cdot7$; S'' (surface after eight days)$=6\cdot5$ therefore $S'-S''=4\cdot2$ and

$$\frac{S'-S''}{S'\times t} = \frac{4\cdot2}{10\cdot7\times4} = 0\cdot098.$$

The difference is slight, but nevertheless exists. The same calculation made for the fourth period gives 0·119, the fifth period gives 0·136 and the sixth 0·175 (the area of the wound is now equal to one square centimetre). It was obvious that I was far from having a constant to deal with. Fig. 14 clearly shows the extent of my error in the shaded area. This error, as can be seen, was considerable and affected the last figure calculated by 100 per cent (0·67 instead of 0·33). On other wounds it was still more important.

All the values of S which could be derived from the formula were too high. Hence, it was clear that it was the denominator which must be augmented. But it could not be increased by a constant coefficient, for the values of the entire formula mounted progressively, from 0·085 to 0·175. Therefore I had to find a correcting factor which increased in proportion as the wound diminished.

On second thought, this was logical, for I already knew from a number of experiments that the most important factor

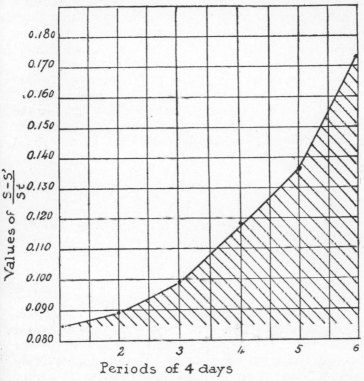

FIG. 14. CALCULATION OF THE FORMULA

in the rate of cicatrization was the size. Now, in our example, formula (2) was established for a wound of a certain dimension: 16·2 cm.². At the end of twenty days its size was reduced to 1 cm.². It was therefore obvious that the first formula could no longer be considered as valid. The correcting factor had to be a function of the actual area of the wound; and as this area was precisely our unknown factor, it could not be utilized.

I realized, however, that if the area itself could not be used, there existed an element which increased regularly as the area diminished and that the surface was necessarily a function of this element. It was what can be called the *age of the wound*, namely the number of days gone by since the beginning of the experiment, since the moment when the wound has become bacteriologically sterile. This age could be known at all times. Unfortunately it increased much more rapidly than was necessary. I fell into the opposite extreme and obtained decreasing values with my formula. However, by turning over this problem from all angles I noticed that the discrepancies increased as a *reciprocal function of the square root of the successive surfaces*. The solution was at hand. The decrease of the surface being a function of the time, it sufficed to introduce in the denominator the square root of the age of the wound, necessarily a reciprocal function of the square root of the areas.

By means of an artifice, I thus replaced the area by a factor on which it depended quantitatively, and I corrected the formula in function of its decreasing size, without taking anything but the age into consideration.

It must be admitted that I had been very lucky. The correction was much simpler than I had thought. I never imagined, when first checking the new formula, that it would be unnecessary to introduce auxiliary constants, which are the terror of physicists, for they are the proof that the mechanism of the phenomenon is far from being solved. I thought I was only nearing the solution when I wrote the equation

$$\frac{S-S'}{S(t+\sqrt{T})}=k \quad \dots\dots\dots\dots\dots\dots(3)$$

T being the number of days since the beginning or the age of the wound and k the coefficient which had to be stabilized, I immediately deduced from formula (3) the value S'' of the surface at the time T'

$$S'' = S'[1 - k(t + \sqrt{T'})] \quad \ldots\ldots\ldots\ldots\ldots(4)$$

This would enable me to calculate the curve from point to point with only two values of the surface of the wound at t days' interval to start from. Practically, t is always chosen equal to 4. I immediately verified this formula on a certain number of experimental curves. The accord from one end to the other was good, much better than I had hoped. I could thus, by means of a simple formula, containing only one coefficient, k (which, we will soon see, possessed the advantage of not being arbitrary), express, as a function of time, the evolution of a very complex phenomenon. This was unforeseen. At the beginning of my studies I thought it would be necessary to resort to many more arbitrary coefficients. Here is a convincing example of the fact that a definite phenomenon taken as a whole, can often obey a simple law, even though it is the result of an important number of factors, each of which obeys laws which can individually be more complicated. We are almost on the verge of touching that amazing and disturbing co-ordination which characterizes living beings.

The first practical application of the formula was the study of antiseptics. It enabled us to establish rapidly the real qualities of preconized antiseptics and to prick a number of soap bubbles such as the 'cicatrizing agents' reputed for accelerating the healing of wounds.

We soon became convinced at Hospital 21 that, out of approximately two hundred substances tried, only two possessed an exceptional number of qualities: the nos. 30 and 142, as stated before. The formula only confirmed the choice already made empirically. The method employed for these experiments was the following one.[1] A wound was sterilized with Dakin's solution, prepared according to Daufresne's method, or with 'Chloramine T'. The curve was calculated

---

[1] All technical details have been given in A. Carrel and Dehelly's book, *Le traitement des plaies infectées* (Masson, 1917. Collection Horizon). We also experimented on the action of sunlight, of artificial light, of ultra-violet rays and of oxygen. In no case could we detect any acceleration whatsoever.

from beginning to end. When, after about eight days, we felt sure that the wound was healing 'normally' we replaced the standard dressing by another one with the antiseptic to be tried out. If there was a slowing up of the cicatrization, that is to say, a difference between the calculated figures and those of the area measured, it indicated either that the new sub-

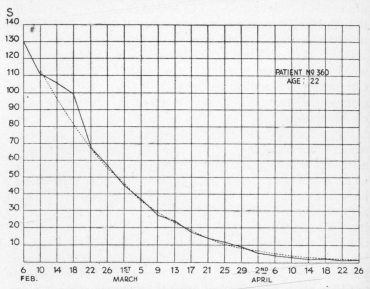

FIG. 15. LARGE ABDOMINAL WOUND, CICATRIZED IN THREE MONTHS. IMPORTANT INFECTION FROM THE 10TH TO THE 18TH OF FEBRUARY, FOLLOWED, AFTER STERILIZATION, BY A RAPID ACCELERATION

stances had not maintained the bacteriological sterility (this fact was controlled microscopically) or else that it was irritating and impeded epithelization. To be certain that the discrepancy was not due to other factors, the dressings with the Dakin or Chloramine solution were reapplied for four or eight days. In general, these dressings not only brought the cicatrization curve back to normal but *determined an acceleration which caused it to catch up with lost time.* That is, when the irritation due to infection had not lasted too long. This was absolutely unforeseen. Fig. 15, which represents the evolution of an abdominal wound on a soldier twenty-two years old (no. 360), shows that the accord between the experiment and the calculation was excellent during nearly three months. The date of complete cicatrization was calculated on the 10th of February and gave the 6th of May as an answer. On the 30th of April the wound had an area of 0·70 cm.^{2} and the calculated figure was 0·75. It was completely healed on the 4th of May instead of the 6th, an error of two days out of ninety. An important divergence can be noticed between the 10th and 18th of February due to a re-infection of the wound, which at that time was kept under a plain sterile dressing. Chloramine was applied on the 18th, and the rate was immediately accelerated. The curve overtook the calculated point on the 22nd.[1]

Fig. 16 shows an experiment with Flavine, an antiseptic which was much praised at the time in England. The experiment was begun on the 23rd of April, after a small infection which manifested itself on the 15th by a slight retardation had been conquered. The result was almost immediate. On the 25th of May not only had the wound ceased to cicatrize but it had enlarged (from 4·3 to 5·2 cm.^{2}). The immediate application of Chloramine brought about the renewal of cicatrization by epidermization. On the 1st of May another trial brought about another stop. On the 3rd of May we definitely resorted to Chloramine, which brought the experimental curve back to the calculated one. During all this time the wound had remained sterile. From a purely antiseptic point of view, Flavine was therefore excellent. But, on the other hand, its necrotic action was so strong that it was impossible to employ it. We could therefore, in a few days, establish mathematically, without possible discussion, the real *practical* value of a

---

[1] This interesting phenomenon is not due to the specific action of the Chloramine or Dakin solutions, but to the elimination of the retarding factors, infection or irritation. It is as if the wound accumulated the necessary elements during the slowing up process, and liberated them as soon as the inhibiting cause was suppressed. The same phenomenon can be observed in the growth of living beings when an impediment which retards their growth is eliminated.

treatment. It was possible, for the first time, to settle, by measurements and calculations, discussions in which self-conceit and sentimental reasons had up till then played the principal part.

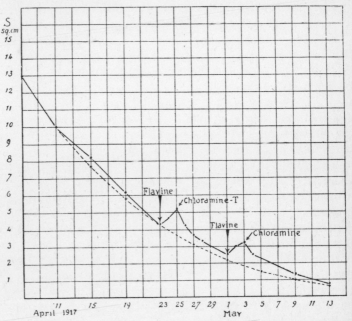

FIG. 16. INFLUENCE OF DIFFERENT ANTISEPTICS ON A WOUND

Now that I have explained the practical applications of the method, I will turn back again to the study of the formula itself and show what could be derived from it.

CHAPTER VI

INDEX OF CICATRIZATION—INFLUENCE OF THE AGE OF THE PATIENT—INFLUENCE OF THE SIZE OF THE WOUND

WE have seen that the first part of the problem consisted in finding a parameter remaining constant throughout the entire phenomenon of cicatrization. Now the coefficient k, constant for a given wound, seemed to vary from one wound to another and from one man to another. As, however, it characterized the rate at which a certain wound healed, I replaced it by the letter i and named it *index of cicatrization.*

I naturally asked myself whether this index was solely characteristic of each wound studied or whether it possessed a more general and hidden significance. To solve this new problem, I drew up a table in which were brought together certain known elements corresponding to completed experiments: index, dimension of the wound (area in cm.^{2}), and age of the patient. I had already observed that the younger a man was the quicker he cicatrized. It was therefore natural to try to see whether the index did not, to a certain extent, depend on the age of the man. The two following facts were soon well established:

1.—Small wounds cicatrized more rapidly in relative values than large ones; their index was therefore higher than that of larger wounds.

2.—Wounds of the same area cicatrized more rapidly on a young man than on an older man. The index i was therefore a function of age as well as of the area of the wound.

These observations were of interest because the importance of the index would be much increased if it could be proved that it was not an individual factor but depended, on the contrary, on general factors such as the area of the wound and the age of the patient. If it had been a function of the state of health of the patient, of the extent of his physical resistance, of his antecedents, there would have been an index for each person and for each wound. This would have eliminated all possibility of connecting this constant to measurable physiological factors, and would, in consequence, have materially reduced its importance. No scientific laws would exist if there were only particular cases. On the other hand, it seemed rather strange that the general condition of the patient did not influence the activity of reparation.

A close examination of the wounded cared for at the hospital clearly demonstrated that outside of certain specific cases, such as diabetes, syphilis (in periods of accidents), and inveterate alcoholism, the activity of reparation expressed by the index appeared to be solely determined by the age of the patient and the area of the wound. At any rate, the fluctuations due to other factors were negligible in the experimental conditions in which we placed ourselves. They were of an order of magnitude inferior to the tolerable experimental errors.

This unlooked-for result was partly due to the fact that all our patients with few exceptions were soldiers, that is to say, healthy men in the prime of age, between twenty and forty years old. What is more, in spite of the hardships, the life they led was healthy when compared to the stagnant life in towns with all its excesses. The majority were robust peasants, accustomed to live out of doors. The others, nervous and morally tired city men, had generally become stouter and gained in health. We were therefore dealing with a selection. But this selection gave us precisely what would have been very difficult to find in peace-time, namely normality. However, I may say that I had several occasions of studying all sorts of different wounds after the end of the war, such as eschars, wounds which do not heal normally, varicose ulcers, burns, etc., on men unfit for military service. The discrepancies observed between the 'normal' index and the calculated index were much less frequent than I had supposed.

Sufficient elements were on hand to make it possible to

establish a chart or, in other words, to draw on squared paper a 'family' of curves as a function of the index and of the area of the wound. Each curve corresponded to a determined age between twenty and forty. Fig. 17 represents this chart. To find the index of cicatrization corresponding to a given wound of known area, a line parallel to the abscissae or axis of the

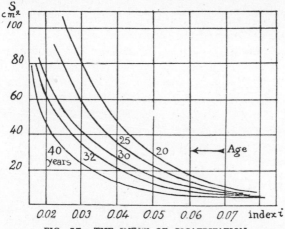

FIG. 17. THE INDEX OF CICATRIZATION

indices (horizontal) is drawn up to the point of junction with the curve representing the age of the patient. From this point a perpendicular is drawn on to the same axis and its intersection with this axis (abscissae) gives the value of the index. For example, a wound 60 centimetres square on a man twenty-five years old, corresponds to a 'normal' index of 0·03. The same wound on a man of thirty-two will have an index of 0·02.

This represented an improvement from several points of view. First of all, the reader will remember that two measurements of the area were necessary to calculate the index by means of formula (3). The quantity cicatrized in four days had to be known (experience showed that this lapse of time was necessary and sufficient). With the chart there was no need to let four days elapse. The calculation was made at the start. In the second place, this procedure presented another advantage besides that of simplicity and economy of time, namely, that of precision. For, if two measurements are made at four days' interval, it may happen that during this time slight incidents escaping our observation occur, which can momentarily retard or accelerate cicatrization. The index calculated from the amount cicatrized during those four days will therefore be inaccurate, and the whole curve equally so. As we have seen above, a wound comes back to its normal rate when the local causes of perturbation are eliminated. The index furnished by the chart is independent of this cause of error.

I spoke of retardation, which can be due to a traumatism or to infection, and also of acceleration. This latter phenomenon takes place, for example, when a wound rapidly epithelizes small crannies like those represented in Fig. 18. The figures below show the error that would have been made if the index had been calculated between the 20th and 24th of May (the patient was thirty-one years old).

1916	May 20th	May 24th	May 27th	June 1st	June 5th
Area observed . .	34·5	24·8	20·6	17·0	13·1
„ calculated (index taken from the chart)	34·5	29·2	22·4	17·4	13·1
Area (index computed from formula (3)) .	34·5	24·8	16·8	10·9	6·8

If the index obtained from the chart is used, the discrepancy between the two figures on the 24th of May is wiped out on the 5th of June. The theoretical index obtained from the chart was 0·032. That given by calculation was 0·047. The error would therefore have been important, and the use of the chart eliminates it completely. Finally, this method has the following third serious advantage. The index obtained from the chart being a mean value, corresponding to a normal asceptic cicatrization on a normal individual, if, independently of all known errors, a more or less important discrepancy is observed between this index and that of the wound itself calculated by means of formula (3) it will be the indication that the patient *is not normal*. There is an unknown retarding cause which it may be interesting to investigate. And if there

Patient N°488 .Age: 31 , i = 0.03

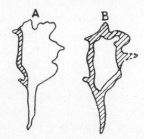

FIG. 18. (A) ASPECT OF THE WOUND ON MAY 20TH. ONLY THE SHADED PARTS ARE CICATRIZED. AREA IS EQUAL TO 34.5 SQ. CM. (B) ASPECT OF THE WOUND ON MAY 24TH. IN FOUR DAYS IT HAS CICATRIZED ITS NARROW PARTS. AREA EQUALS 24.8 SQ. CM.

is every reason to admit that the man is in good health it will be *the proof that his real physiological age is not the same as his legal, official age*. In other words, from then on, there was a way of determining the difference between these two ages expressed by the reparation activity of tissues. Later on I will deal with this point more thoroughly. In connexion with this subject, however, I would like to mention the first calculated determination of the age of a man. The great and regretted surgeon, Dr. Tuffier, had put an engineer, Dr. Desmarres, in charge of the calculations relative to wounds. One day, in Compiègne, I received a letter containing an experimental curve of cicatrization and asking for an explanation. The curve calculated by means of the first formula had given a time of cicatrization materially longer than that actually observed.

I had studied only a few days before long and narrow wounds which, as we have already seen, cicatrize more rapidly than others, by reason of the proximity of the epithelial borders. I immediately concluded that the wound in question was of this shape, and although I had not seen the drawings I introduced the new correction (of which I shall speak presently) and obtained a good accord. Having satisfied myself that an elongated shape was probably the cause of the acceleration, I consulted the chart and saw that the index corresponded to about twenty years of age. Dr. Tuffier had not as yet heard of the results obtained on the subject of age. I therefore replied by telling him that his patient, assuming that he was in good general health, must be between twenty and twenty-two years old, and that his wound was long and narrow. Very much surprised, Tuffier answered by a letter in which he confirmed the exactitude of the calculation. The wounded man in question was a young soldier called Jacquemaire, twenty-one years old and Clemenceau's grandson.

It was therefore possible by this method to determine the age of a wounded man with a good approximation.

These experiments, first performed on men, were taken up again on animals and gave similar results. When, owing to the fact that we had no facilities for breeding, it was impossible to be certain of the age of the animals, the latter was replaced by the weight, which in young animals is very nearly proportional to age. On guinea-pigs, for example, we obtained for wounds of the same order of magnitude (1 to 1·5 cm.²) the following values (the guinea-pig weighing 250 gr. was only a few weeks old).

Weight (in grams.)			800	680	560	250
Initial area (in sq. cm.)			1·5	1·5	1·0	1·1
Index			0·046	0·075	0·078	0·113

The part played by the size of the wound is most interesting. Wounds which are too large in comparison to the total surface of the body of a man or an animal, do not cicatrize. Everything occurs as if nature had not anticipated the reparation of

CALCULATION OF THE CURVE OF CICATRIZATION
Table giving the Two Coefficients of the Formula
$$S' = S\,[1 - i\,(t + \sqrt{nt})]^{1}$$

Area of Wound	1st Coefficient—Index of Cicatrization i — Age of Patient					2nd Coefficient Time Coefficient $t + \sqrt{nt}$
	20 years	25 years	30 years	32 years	40 years	
sq. cm. 150 and over	0·02	0·02	0·02	0·02	0·02	6 6·81 7·43
140	0·021	0·02	0·02	0·02	0·02	8·00 8·45
130	0·022	0·02	0·02	0·02	0·02	8·90 9·3
120	0·0225	0·02	0·02	0·02	0·02	9·65 10·00
110	0·0240	0·02	0·02	0·02	0·02	10·32 10·64
100	0 025	0·02	0·02	0·02	0·02	10·93 11·21
90	0·0275	0·022	0·02	0·02	0·02	11·48 11·75
80	0·03	0·023	0·02	0·02	0·02	12·00 12·25
70	0·0325	0·025	0·02	0·02	0·02	12·48 12·72
60	0·0355	0·03	0·0225	0·02	0·02	12·95 13·16
50	0·04	0·034	0·0265	0·0230	0·02	13·37 13·60
40	0·0445	0·04	0·031	0·027	0·022	
30	0·05	0·045	0·0375	0·033	0·026	
25	0·054	0·05	0·04	0·0375	0·029	
20	0·058	0·054	0·0465	0·0425	0·0325	
15	0·0645	0·06	0·0525	0·0475	0·038	
10	0·07	0·066	0·0625	0·055	0·045	
5 and under	0·08	0·075	0·07	0·07	0·07	

[1] du Noüy, *J. Exp. Med.*, 1916, xxiv, 451, 461; 1917, xxv, 721.

lesions, the dimensions of which are too important. The index of wounds decreases progressively until it reaches a constant value, namely: 0·02. It may decrease still further, but we have no experimental facts to prove it. The largest wounds which I was able to study did not attain 150 square centimetres. But the maximum size of wounds affected by the index 0·02 is not the same for every age. A man twenty years old will cicatrize a wound of 150 square centimetres, and over, with an index of 0·02, whereas the same index characterizes a wound of 50 cm.^{2} on a man forty years old.

Age, therefore, introduces important factors of retardation into the rate of cicatrization. The table on page 85 shows the extent of this action.

I had established it to facilitate the calculation of the curves by means of formula (4). It can be seen that all the values of $t+\sqrt{nt}$ (where $nt=T$ the age of the wound, and $t=4$ days) are calculated in advance for $24\times4=96$ days (last column). Under these conditions the calculation was rapid.

A 'family of curves' represented by Fig. 19 can be drawn from this table. In the first place their geometric regularity is impressive. It is striking that such clear quantitative relations between the area of the wound, the age of the patient and the index, can be obtained in a phenomenon as complex as cicatrization. But the curves themselves are most instructive, and propound new problems which we are incapable of solving, for they depend on questions of a much more general order. For instance, what is the signification of the highest curve which corresponds to index 0·02? It signifies that all wounds which give points located in the upper shaded region cicatrize with the same index, or at any rate with an index very close to 0·02. It can be seen that above 150 cm.^{2}, age no longer seems to play any part between twenty and forty years. But though I have no proof of the fact, it is very probable that a wound of this size should heal much more slowly in a man of forty. There is no doubt that things are quite different on either side of this curve and in my experiments I was unable to find indices inferior to 0·02 except in pathological cases, or else when the wound was situated in certain regions practically deprived of underlying conjunctive tissue: the skull, the foot, etc. Therefore on the right hand side of the curve the primary factors of age and area no longer intervene quantitatively. There are unknown factors, and reparation is very

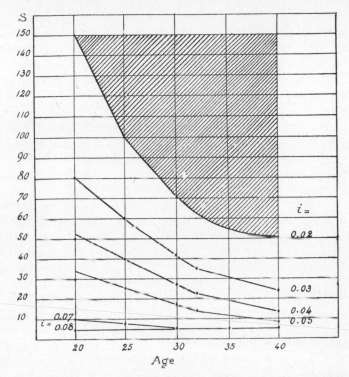

FIG. 19. INFLUENCE OF THE AGE OF THE PATIENT AND OF THE
SIZE OF THE WOUND

slow in all cases. On the left-hand side of the curve, on the contrary, everything occurs as if these two factors were the only ones that entered into play, and the considerable importance of age can be seen, especially in the first curve (0·02). But one can also observe that the influence of age decreases rapidly with the dimensions of the wound and that, when the area is inferior to 5 square centimetres, the wounds cicatrize at about the same rate between twenty and forty years of age. In this case, as in the case of large wounds, age and area lose their importance. In wounds less than 5 cm.² in size, the

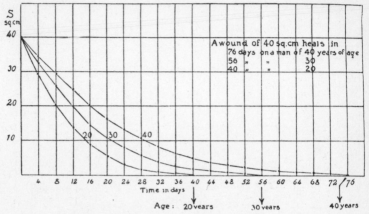

FIG. 20. RATE OF HEALING AS A FUNCTION OF THE AGE OF THE
PATIENT

edges are so close that almost all the work of reparation is due to epidermization. Towards the end of this book we will see that many years later, in 1933, I eliminated the area so as to obtain a new index depending only on the age.

To recapitulate the foregoing pages clearly it suffices to glance at Figs. 20 and 21. The first expresses the role of age in the rate of reparation of a wound of 40 cm.². The second, the role of the area, the age and other conditions being identical.

. . . . .

In reference to the problem propounded by Prof. Tuffier, I pointed out that it had been necessary to introduce a correction in the case of long and narrow wounds resulting, for instance, from longitudinal incisions along the muscles. We

saw in the first chapter on cicatrization when speaking of
Carrel's experiments, that epithelization is activated by the
proximity of the epithelial edges.   This enabled us to understand the double part played by grafts of skin.   It was therefore important to take this into account, the total gain on the

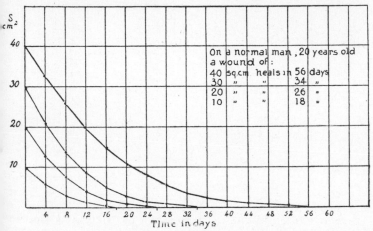

FIG. 21.   RATE OF HEALING AS A FUNCTION OF THE SIZE OF THE
WOUND

date calculated being from twelve to sixteen days.   Now, the
principal difference from a quantitative point of view between
such a wound and one that is round or square is that the perimeter, the length of the epithelial edge, is increased with
respect to the area of the wound.   It is therefore the *shape*
which plays a part, for no perceptible differences are observed
between wounds that are more or less indented, outside of
sudden but momentary accelerations such as the one mentioned
on page 82.

I observed that the phenomenon of acceleration with respect
to the curve calculated by means of formula (4) only begins to
show slightly when the length is eight or nine times greater
than the width.   When the ratio is equal to 10 (length 10 cm.,
breadth 1 cm. for example), it becomes very apparent.   It

continues to increase, and reaches a maximum value when the ratio approaches 20. At that moment, cicatrization is almost complete and the absolute value of the correction is very close to 1 cm.[2], this being a maximum.

Therefore the maximum correction could be expressed by $\frac{1}{20}\frac{L}{l}=1$ (as the ratio $\frac{L \text{ (length)}}{l \text{ (width)}}=20$). This empirical correction had to be subtracted from the figure normally calculated

Patient N° 409

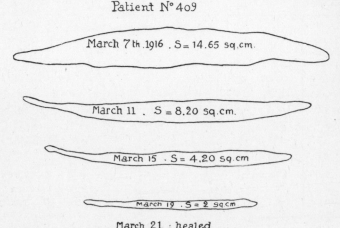

March 7th.1916 . S = 14.65 sq.cm.

March 11 . S = 8.20 sq.cm.

March 15 . S = 4.20 sq.cm

March 19 . S = 2 sq.cm

March 21 : healed

FIG. 22. LONG AND NARROW WOUND. RAPID CICATRIZATION

by means of formula (4). But I could introduce neither L nor l in the formula, as it was impossible to know at the start what would be the length and the width of the wound at the end of a time x. Therefore another way of expressing the same thing had to be found.

Now, in such wounds the perimeter—let us call it P—is practically equal to twice the length, or $P=2L$, and P being a function of the square root of the area and of a certain coefficient which depends on the shape of the wound, one could write:

$$L=k\sqrt{S}$$

where k is a coefficient to be determined experimentally. It is superfluous to enter into the details of the calculations which finally led me to admit that the correction could be satisfactorily expressed by $\dfrac{\sqrt{S}}{S}$ which it sufficed to subtract from formula (4). It may be of interest to give the reader a few figures enabling him to realize that the accord thus obtained is quite satisfactory. (Patient no. 409) Fig. 22 represents the successive aspects of the wound. The table below gives the figures.

Date	Area S	$\sqrt{S}$	Width l	L'gth L	$\dfrac{\sqrt{S}}{S}$	Area calc. without correc.	Area calc. with correc.
March	sq. cm.		cm.			sq. cm.	sq. cm.
7	14·6	3·70	1·4	12·0	0·25	,,	,,
11	8·2	2·86	0·9	11·0	0·35	8·5	8·20
15	4·3	2·07	0·5	9·5	0·48	4·4	3·95
19	2·0	1·41	0·25	6·6	0·70	2·1	1·40
21	0·0					1·4	0 cic.
23	0					0·9	
27	0					0·6	
31	0					cicatrized	

The formula for ordinary wounds gave March 31st as the date of total cicatrization, or an error of ten days.

The corrected general formula, which became

$$S_n = S_{n-1}[1 - i(t + \sqrt{nt})] - \frac{\sqrt{S_n}}{S} \quad\quad\quad\quad(5)$$

possessed the advantage of admitting a zero, whereas the current formula, being asymptotic, forced one to admit that the wound was cicatrized when the calculation gave a figure inferior to 0·4 cm.^{2}, for example.

What is more, the correction is so slight for wounds in which the ratio $\dfrac{L}{l}$ is small (it is never inferior to 1) that it can be introduced at any moment, as soon as it is observed that the wound, long at the outset, shrinks rapidly. Not only is it altogether negligible for large wounds, but by reason of the form of the formula itself its action is compensated and it enters automatically into play the minute it becomes useful.

I may add that from a practical point of view these calculations would be tedious did the slide rule not exist. Without this marvellous tool it would have been much more difficult and would have taken much longer to solve these problems. Moreover, my mathematical treatment of them was not in the least classical: the formula is not homogeneous, and a true mathematician would probably judge my method rather severely. That is why I endeavoured to find a more elegant procedure. The reader will soon see that I succeeded in obtaining a general equation of classical aspect. I rarely employed it, however, for it is much less convenient than the first, and requires two coefficients instead of one.

.   .   .   .   .

Meanwhile, I was sent to the Rockefeller Institute in New York for a stay of several weeks. During this time I applied my formula to study the cicatrization of civilian wounds and in particular of varicose ulcers.

I was able to verify that these wounds of pathological origin cicatrized according to the formula as soon as they were disinfected. Curiously enough, in certain cases the cicatrization was more rapid—there was a higher index—than would have been the case in a war wound, that is to say, in a fresh wound. It seemed as if nature had accumulated materials during the long period in which the infected ulcer did not cicatrize, which sterilization suddenly freed. We had already observed this phenomenon in conjunction with momentary infections of wounds previously sterile. (See Fig. 15.)

The new problem which now confronted me was the establishment of a true equation of the curve. The one of which we have spoken so far rendered great services and had a real practical value. But it did not permit me to calculate the area at a given moment; neither could I obtain the date of cicatrization directly, without passing by intermediary points. I had to proceed point by point. It was an extrapolation formula.

I spent several weeks in search of the ideal general equation. By 'ideal' I mean that it must not have more than two coefficients and that these coefficients must necessarily be functions of the index i, which had a well-determined significance and was itself a function of the age of the patient. I was especially anxious to obtain these coefficients without calculation, by means of a chart. It was necessary that they should not be arbitrary. It is always possible with a little patience to find an equation by increasing the number of arbitrary coefficients. But the interest of a formula is then much slighter. A little farther on I will mention such a case.

Mr. de Rufz de Lavison, to whom I exposed my difficulties, agreed to collaborate with me in this work. A few weeks later he brought me an equation which was satisfactory from the point of view of the accord with the observed facts. Unfortunately it contained two coefficients which I could not connect with the values of i. This equation was the following:

$$T = k_1 \mathrm{Log}_e \frac{S_0}{S} + 2k_2(\sqrt{S_0} - \sqrt{S}).$$

It can be seen that it gives the time elapsed T instead of the area of the wound. To obtain the date of total cicatrization it sufficed to replace S by 0·4 or 0·3, and T was obtained in days. This result encouraged me to take up my calculations anew in another way, and this is how I attempted to do it.

Let us admit that during a very short time dt (the differential notation is here employed) the cicatrized area ds remains proportional to the total area. This is written in the following way:

$$-ds = KSdt$$

from which by integration with respect to time one obtains:

$$T = -\int_{S_0}^{S} \frac{ds}{KS}$$

or
$$T = -\frac{1}{K} \int_{S_0}^{S} \frac{ds}{S}$$

which is equivalent to $T = \frac{1}{K} Log_e \frac{S_0}{S}$

or
$$KT = Log_e \frac{S_0}{S,}$$

which can be written
$$S = S_0 e^{-KT},$$

e being the base of natural logarithms.

In calculating the values of K for different values of T, one sees that this coefficient increases regularly. This equation, as could be expected, does not express the facts, and gives for each value of T (the age of the wound) values of S which differ more and more from those calculated by the extrapolation formula:

$$S_n = S_{n-1}[1 - i (t + \sqrt{nt})]............................ (4)$$

It was therefore necessary to introduce another coefficient which would correct the divergence as cicatrization progressed. This coefficient had to be incorporated preferably into the formula as an exponent. But here a problem immediately arose. Was it better to attempt to find this correction by giving to T its real value and by studying the law of the variations of K, or was it better to maintain K constant and to study the variations of a certain coefficient α entering into the exponent in the following manner:

$$-K(T + \alpha).$$

I tried the two methods. The first revealed itself as not practical because the coefficient being small (of the order of 0·020) with respect to the time T, the smallest numerical variations were of sufficient importance to destroy the concordance of the curves. In other words, this correction was too sensitive. In the second case, on the contrary, fairly important variations in a certain coefficient K_2 connected with α by a relation such as

$$\alpha = \frac{T^2}{K_2}$$

interfered very little with the accuracy of the calculation of the entire formula.

This result was obtained by plotting on squared paper the values of α as ordinates. These values were computed from the formula:

$$\alpha = \frac{Log\dfrac{S_0}{S}}{K} - T = \frac{1}{K} Log\frac{S_0}{S} - T$$

The time T was plotted as abscissae.

We thus obtained a curve expressing the law of divergencies between the formula

$$S = S_0 e^{-KT}$$

and the formula

$$S_n = S_{n-1}[1 - i(t + \sqrt{nt})].$$

Now this curve (Fig. 23) is simply a perfect parabola answering the classical equation $y^2 = 2px$, ($y = T$ and $x = \alpha$), which is equal to saying that

$$\alpha = \frac{T^2}{2p}$$

And in consequence the general equation of the curve became

$$S = S_0 e^{-K\left(T + \frac{T^2}{2p}\right)} \quad \dots\dots\dots\dots\dots\dots (6)$$

It was possible from now on to calculate directly the area of a wound at any date. To obtain the date of complete cicatrization, it sufficed to solve the equation making $S = 0.4$, as a wound of 0.4 square centimetres cicatrizes in less than twenty-four hours.

The two coefficients K and p were bound to the index of cicatrization i by simple relations, and one could either calculate them directly, from the above formulae, or else compute them from the values of i found in the chart. The study and discussion of the two coefficients would require too much space and I therefore refer the reader to the original paper.[1]

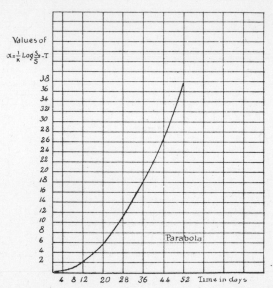

Values of
$$\alpha = \frac{1}{K} Log \frac{S_2}{S} - T$$

FIG. 23. CORRECTING FACTOR IN EQUATION (6)

The concordance between the curves calculated by the extrapolation formula (4) and those obtained by the exponential equation (6) is excellent, as shown by the table below.

But there is another advantage in employing this equation. It may be remembered that the phenomenon of reparation is due to a double process. First, contraction and second, epidermization. The two formulae, (4) and (6), translate into mathematical language the result due to the combined mechanisms. It would be too long and fatiguing for the

[1] Lecomte du Noüy, 'A general equation for the law of cicatrization of surface wounds'. *Journ. of Experimental Medicine*, vol. 29, p. 392 (1919).

TABLE SHOWING THE CONCORDANCE OBTAINED IN CALCULATING THE CURVE OF CICATRIZATION OF A WOUND BY MEANS OF EQUATION NO. 4 AND OF EQUATION NO. 6

Patient No. 263 $i=0.0205$; $k=0.014$; $2p=85$.

Time in days	0	4	8	12	16	20	24	28	32	36
Equation no. 4 (formula of extrapolation) sq. cm.	61·8	50·8	41·4	33·4	26·8	21·2	16·7	13·1	10·2	7·7
Exponential equation, no. 6	61·8	51·0	41·6	33·6	26·9	21·3	16·7	13·1	10·2	7·7

Patient No. 263 (*continued*)

Time in days	40	44	48	52	56	60	64	68	72	76
Equation no. 4 (formula of extrapolation) sq. cm.	6·0	4·5	3·4	2·5	1·8	1·4	1·0	0·7	0·5	0·4
Exponential equation, no. 6	6·0	4·5	3·4	2·5	1·8	1·4	1·0	0·7	0·5	0·4

reader to go into the details of the reasoning which led me to emit the hypothesis that the simple formula

$$S = S_0 e^{-KT}$$

quantitatively expressed the result due to the granular contraction and that the factor $\dfrac{T^2}{2p}$ in the exponent expressed the acceleration due to epidermization. The comparison of the two curves calculated by means of the experimental curves and representing, on the one hand, the diminution of area due to contraction, and, on the other hand, the total phenomenon, contraction+epidermization, proved that this hypothesis was justified. We could thus express the two processes independently,[1] and the last formula was more complete and more satisfactory than the first, though less easy to use.

I have already pointed out some practical applications of these calculations. A few years later they enabled my friend Dr. Ebeling, of the Rockefeller Institute, to demonstrate clearly that the mechanisms which are at the base of all cellular reparation are of a chemical nature. This was done in the following fashion.[2]

It is known that all chemical phenomena are characterized by a 'temperature coefficient', the value of which is about 2·5 (Van't Hoff's coefficient). This means that for every rise in temperature of 10° C. the rate of the reaction is a little more than doubled. Conversely, for every diminution of 10° C., the rate of the reaction is divided by a factor approximately equal to 2·5. This criterium is used when one does not exactly know how to interpret a new phenomenon nor what hypotheses can be eliminated a priori. For example, in the early days of radio-activity, before 1900, scientists began by trying to measure the temperature coefficient. But no matter what the temperature of the reaction, one hundred degrees below zero or several hundred degrees above, the rate of the phenomenon remained the same. The production of what

---

[1] Lecomte du Noüy, loc. cit., *Journ. of Exp. Medicine*, 1919.
[2] A. H. Ebeling, *Journ. of Exp. Medicine*, vol. 35, p. 657 (1922).

were then called the α, β, and γ rays remained immutable. The conclusion, without possible doubt, was that this was *not* a chemical phenomenon but a phenomenon of atomic disintegration. The same is true of the photo-electric phenomenon, known as the Hertz-Hallwachs effect, which consists in the discharge of a conductor of polished zinc, electrically isolated and on which falls a beam of ultra-violet light. By varying the temperature it was proved that this was purely an electronic phenomenon and not a result of combination or decomposition.

The problem was less easy to solve in the case of cicatrization, for it was necessary to work over a range of 10° or 15° C. This immediately eliminated all 'warm-blooded' animals, which could be more correctly called 'thermo-stable' animals.

But there are a quantity of so-called 'cold-blooded' animals. These animals are not characterized by the fact that their blood is cold, which does not signify much, but by the fact that their blood maintains itself approximately at the temperature of the surrounding medium. The reader is aware that insects, fish, reptiles, and batrachians belong to this class. They are deprived of the property of maintaining their temperature constant. For evident reasons it was impossible to work on insects or fish. But in the class of reptiles, alligators and crocodiles were particularly indicated, for they can be kept without difficulty at temperatures varying between 10° and 40° C. At 10° C. they are somnolent and in a state of latent life. At 40° C. they are in full activity.

Square, easily measurable wounds were cut out on the abdomens of young Florida alligators and curves were established. The animals were kept at temperatures constant from beginning to end of each experiment, but variable for each new wound.

It was found that the rate of cicatrization varied in the mean ratio of 2·12 (extremes: 2·47 and 1·88) when the temperature was raised or lowered by 10° C. For instance, at 23° C., a crocodile weighing 314 grams cicatrized a wound of 1·3 square centimetres in 29 days and the same animal at 38° C. (that is, a difference of 15° C.) took only 11 days to cicatrize a wound of 1·2 square centimetres. *Chemical phenomena are therefore at the base of the phenomena of tissue reparation.* This was to be expected; but in biology, as in all sciences in general, facts alone must be considered. Farther on, we shall see that this observation, together with another one equally based on Van't Hoff's coefficient, constitutes one of the most solid links in our reasoning concerning the appreciation of time.

.   .   .   .

The most important facts to be remembered in the preceding pages are, first, that the evolution as a function of time of a physiological phenomenon as complex as cellular reparation, which involves the co-ordination, for a determined end, of a series of physical, chemical, and biological mechanisms, can be mathematically expressed by a very simple formula containing only one well-defined coefficient. Secondly, that this coefficient is a function of the *physiological age*, and that therefore it becomes possible to measure the process of ageing. I do not mention the relationship to the area of the wound, for we shall see, in the last chapter, that it is easy to eliminate this contingency and to obtain a new constant depending solely on the age.[1]

[1] As a result of our studies, the problem was taken up again by other workers. Certain of the proposed formulae are not worthy of mention. Either they did not express the facts accurately, or else their coefficients are meaningless. The excellent work of Prof. Gaston Backmann, however, must be mentioned. (*Ergebnisse der Physiologie*, vol. 33, pp. 915 and 939, 1931). With the help of my experiments he was able to express the curve of cicatrization by means of a formula established by him to account for phenomena of growth in general. This formula expresses the facts perfectly, and in certain cases follows the experimental curve more accurately than mine. Unfortunately, it necessitates no less than four arbitrary coefficients, which have to be determined for every wound. From my point of view, this suppresses all its interest, for it is less important to be able to calculate the area of a wound within one-tenth of a square centimetre than to be able to have an idea of the principal factors which intervene in the phenomenon. Backmann's formula is the following:

$$\log d = k_0 + k_1 . \log (k_3 - T) + k_2 . \log^2 (k_3 - T)$$

where d=the absolute rate of growth or cicatrization in square centimetres. It can be seen that the calculation of a wound by this formula would take a certain length of time.

I have dwelt at length on the details of these calculations and have taken the reader 'behind the scenes', a thing which by tradition or modesty the scientist usually avoids, because it was necessary that he should have absolute confidence in the results published. This confidence can only be acquired in three ways. By repeating the experiments, by knowing the author personally, or by possessing as many elements as possible to enable one to follow step by step all the reasonings which have led to the final conclusion. The two first methods were difficult of realization, and I was therefore obliged to have recourse to the third.

.   .   .   .   .

In order to define more clearly the notion of time and the mechanism of ageing in certain biological processes as well as to check the results obtained *in vivo*, we shall now study the admirable method of tissue-culture outside the organism, which Carrel established in 1912 at the Rockefeller Institute of New York. I shall be obliged to dwell on it at length, for this method has made it possible to detect the existence of the chemical changes underlying the process of ageing, and also to understand the accumulative processes registering the flow of time. It is therefore a new and indispensable element for our ulterior reasoning.

CHAPTER VII

TISSUE-CULTURE *IN VITRO*

CHAPTER I demonstrated the fundamental differences existing between classical cytology, a science of pure observation which suppresses evolution in time by killing the cells, and what Carrel calls 'the new cytology'. This new experimental science enables the searcher to consider the cells in their environment and to observe the reactions determined by modifications in the surrounding medium, as a function of time. To make a comparison, the classical cytology corresponds to the dissection of corpses, whereas tissue-culture is related to medicine, physiology and, one might even say, to elementary sociology. Taken in a restricted sense, this expression is not exaggerated. Indeed, cinematographic films of cell-cultures have revealed totally unknown and unforeseen facts related to the behaviour of the free cells such as the leucocytes (white cells of the blood) and macrophages. These cells, instead of living in a consistent mass, bound one to another like the tissue-cells, disseminate themselves in the culture-medium 'like children let loose in a school-yard'. The pictures are taken, according to the activity of the culture, every 10, 15, 20, or 30 seconds, during periods varying from 24 to 72 hours. They are projected at the ordinary rate of 16 per second or less. Every motion of the cells is therefore considerably accelerated (from 160 to 500 times or more). It is thus possible to discern unsuspected movements and mutual reactions, otherwise imperceptible, just as in the well-known films which revealed to us the opening of a bud and the blossoming of flowers. Unleashed leucocytes can be observed attacking a nervous fibre which resembles a taut string. The fragile and tenuous fibre is bent by the shocks like the string of a bow in the hand of an archer. One sees the macrophages in blood-plasma surrounding themselves with a large undulating membrane resembling a sequence of wavelets in a calm sea at low tide when they die without breaking on a smooth sandy beach. The meetings, the bumps, the flights, the struggles often ending in absorption, the envelopment of one by the other, are all portrayed. We observe, in short, at a scale of a thousandth of a millimetre, all that we are accustomed to see every day around us.

It is in this sense that one can speak of 'sociology', even though the strict meaning of the word is perhaps different. But I cannot think of any other to replace it adequately.

These observations which enable us to witness the incessant activities of the cells and to assist like an indiscreet onlooker at their birth, nourishment, battles, and death, form a new science of which great things can be expected.

Not only can we contemplate them alive and magnified thousands of times on the screen, but we dispose, thanks to the cinematographic technique, of the apparently superhuman power of contracting their time in comparison to ours. Like the character in a remarkable story by Wells,[1] we can accelerate the rhythm of the life of our constitutive elements.   In other words, we have the faculty of influencing the fourth dimension.

.   .   .   .   .

Different workers, and especially Harrison, had tried before Carrel to maintain pieces of tissue alive outside the organism. But no one succeeded in prolonging the life of these explanted[2] fragments beyond a few days for lack of proper nourishment. It was therefore a momentary extension of life which they obtained, and not an independent and unlimited existence. Dr. Carrel was the first to prevent death setting in. The explanted tissues which are kept in special containers with tremendous aseptic precautions, for one single microbe suffices to infect the culture and to kill it, can be assimilated to immortal experimental animals. We have already mentioned in the first part of this book the fact that a strain of cells derived from a small fraction of embryonic heart in 1912

[1] H. G. Wells, 'The New Accelerator', *Twelve Stories and a Dream*.
[2] See footnote, page 20.

is still alive to-day. The cultures are as young as they ever were and show no signs of ageing as measured by their growth activity, which has not varied since the beginning. There is actually no reason why those fragments of living flesh should ever die, except accidentally. If it were not necessary, as we shall soon see, to cut these cultures in half every two days, if they could have been left to grow unrestrictedly, they would now occupy a literally inconceivable volume. For, as their size doubles in forty-eight hours, they would already have attained   6,130,000,000,000,000,000,000,000,000,000,000,000,000, 000,000,000 cubic metres at the end of the first year (2^{182} cubic millimetres or 613×10^{43}). At the end of twenty-four years the calculated volume would be 2^{4368} or 5,862 followed by one thousand three hundred and three zeros, in cubic metres. At the end of one year they would have been more than thirteen quatrillion times bigger than the sun. I hasten to add that these calculations are absurd and devoid of significance as, if the culture is not periodically divided in two, the growth of volume brings about its death in a few days. Owing to the fact that there is no circulating system, the interior cells are not nourished and cannot eliminate the toxic products resulting from the reactions which they engender. They therefore die, and in doing so liberate poisons which accelerate the death of the other cells. The culture can persist only in very thin layers or in very small fragments where all the exchanges can take place on the surface.

Nevertheless it is possible to experiment indefinitely on the same family of cells proceeding from the same strain. A much greater precision is possible than when operating *in vivo* because of the elimination of innumerable causes of error due to the individual characteristics of animals of different origin. We have already mentioned these advantages in the first chapter, but they are not the only ones inherent to this method.

To preserve these tissues in a state of activity they must be divided at short intervals of time, viz. every other day. Two cultures rigorously identical from a biological point of view are therefore available instead of one. Consequently, for each experiment and for every stage of the experiment, one obtains every second day a control which in turn will be the originator of a new family of cultures, the biological, chemical, and physical properties of which can be compared at any ulterior date with those of the cultures issued from the fragment submitted to experimentation. It is thus possible during a series of experiments lasting several months and bringing about hereditary modifications of the cells (immunity, for instance), to compare cultures proceeding from successive stages of the experiment. The reader is aware that for the majority of biological experiments it is necessary to have one or two controls on which no experiment has been made. This enables one, by comparison, to appreciate the results obtained. But two animals are never identical, whereas the two parts of a same culture are as identical as possible.

This is not all. To study the characteristics and properties of certain species of microbes it is necessary to dispose of pure cultures; that is to say, cultures composed of one kind of microbe excluding every other micro-organism. It is quite evident that, when there is a mixture of different microbes, it is impossible to define the function of each species in the lesions and accidents determined on an animal by the culture. Science has no use for anonymity. Its aim, on the contrary, is to discover responsibilities. It would also be impossible to prepare preventive vaccine or curative sera against *one* of these organisms; in other words, we could not manufacture 'specific' vaccines or sera.

This is equally true of tissue-cultures. To be able to study the cytological and physiological characteristics of a certain species of cells, it is necessary to obtain pure cultures. First, Carrel and then, under his direct guidance, Albert Fischer of Copenhagen, Albert H. Ebeling, Raymond Parker, and one or two others have succeeded in isolating absolutely pure strains of fibroblasts (conjunctive cells), osteoblasts (bone-producing cells), cartilage, epithelium, cancer cells, leucocytes, etc. These strains are generally capable of living indefinitely *in vitro* while reproducing and conserving all their specific characteristics. This fundamental discovery was not accepted without a struggle by certain biologists, particularly in France. A few scientists pretended that it was impossible, simply because their own imperfect techniques had prevented them from succeeding. These facts, however, are now classical and no longer discussed by any one.

I have spoken of 'technique'. It will be necessary to say a few words on the subject so as to enable the reader to follow the mechanism of the experiments on ageing which will be described farther on and which established the link between the experiments on cicatrization and those on tissue-cultures.

The subject of tissue-culture techniques is vast enough to fill a voluminous book written by Fischer, and I shall therefore make a very brief summary. The principle is simple. It consists in cutting out a fragment of living flesh and incorporating it to a medium capable of sustaining and nourishing it. The products of excretion are eliminated by washing every other day and the cultures, divided in two equal parts by cutting with a sharp knife, are then transplanted separately into a new medium. One of them serves as control. The cultures are naturally maintained at the temperature which is normal for the animal from which they proceed (about 38° C. or 100° to 103° F. for chicken embryos).

Realization is less simple. Indeed, as I have already stated, the most important thing was first to find the nutritive medium capable of indefinitely prolonging the life of the cells. Carrel's idea of using *embryonic juice* was a stroke of genius and laid the foundation of the whole method. The 'juice' is obtained by mincing eight-day-old chicken embryos. To this end, fecundated eggs are maintained in an incubator and, after eight days, are brought into the operating room, which must be as dust-free as possible. The operator, masked and in a sterile blouse, breaks the shell after having washed and sterilized it, and extracts the embryo which he cuts into small pieces. These pieces are then crushed (in a 'Latapie' crusher, for instance) and form a kind of pulp which is mixed with a complex, rigorously balanced saline solution. This mixture centrifuged and decanted is the 'embryo juice'. No one so far has ever been able to replace it by any synthetic medium. This product is now also employed medically to avert surgical shocks.

Needless to say, these operations must all be accomplished with infinite aseptic precautions, far greater than for a surgical operation. The preparation of the saline solutions (*Tyrode* and *Ringer* solutions) also demands great care. The substances employed must be rigorously pure and the degree of alkalinity (measured by the concentration in hydrogen ions expressed by the symbol *p*H) is controlled electrically or colorimetrically. In addition to the 'juice' there is also the 'support' which is composed of a drop of coagulated chicken plasma. (We remind the reader that the blood is composed of red and white blood-cells suspended in a liquid called the *plasma*, which coagulates under different influences.) The culture, one or two square millimetres in size, is placed in this drop or on its surface, according to the nature of the cells to be cultivated. The blood is taken from a young and healthy chicken by means of a sterile operation made under anaesthesia. The blood-cells are separated from the plasma by centrifugation in tubes previously paraffined and cooled at 0° C. so as to prevent coagulation.

When these elements have been prepared, all that remains to be done is to take an incubated egg, about nine or ten days old, remove the embryo, dissect the heart, or any other part of the animal, cut out a certain number of small pieces without tearing them and incorporate them on a thin slide into a drop of plasma mixed with a drop of embryo juice. The mica is then covered by a thick glass slide hollowed out in the middle, sealed with hot paraffin, and put into an incubator at 38° C. Forty-eight hours later, the fragments are extracted and cut with a cataract knife, the blade of which is only three millimetres long. They are then washed in Tyrode solution and quickly replanted into a new nutritive drop before the latter has had time to coagulate. This is done every two or three days according to the nature of the tissue. The small pieces of heart, rapidly surrounded by a transparent and fragile circle of new cells, often continue to beat during two or three weeks, sometimes longer. They can be seen through the microscope, contracting spasmodically, and nothing is more impressive than to observe this fundamental and marvellous mechanism which is still so mysterious. This famous experiment gave rise to the legend of the 'ever-beating heart'. But there is no example of these heart fragments having beaten for more than three months. A month is already a limit rarely attained. The beats become more and more distant as the culture ages, and generally last only from fifteen to twenty days. The contracting muscular cells are progressively replaced in the culture by inert cells of conjunctive tissue, the fibroblasts, whose reproductive energy is greater and which finally reign alone. It must not be forgotten that at the end of fifteen days the initial fragment has been cut seven times and that after each division it has reconstituted itself mainly with fibroblasts. At the end of a fortnight, the beats are already much weaker and sometimes only perceptible every ten seconds. They often cease altogether when the culture is examined under the microscope, and the temperature must be raised—for instance, by placing the whole microscope in a small incubator—in order to see them reappear.

Tissue-culture is neither simple nor easy if one wishes to maintain pure strains in good health for any length of time. The technique has been so marvellously perfected by Carrel that it is easy to keep them alive during two or three weeks. The difficulties come later, and it requires a long experience to be able to prolong their existence beyond three months. It even seems as if the difficulties increased with age. This explains the fact that the only laboratory where cultures have been kept alive for twenty-four years is that of Dr. Carrel, which is splendidly organized and has several 'culture doctors'.

For cultures, like human beings, often have slight illnesses. These must be known and the consequences attenuated or annulled. A fatty degeneration shown by the apparition of small refractive globules, or a variation in structure, is an indication that the diet must be momentarily changed and the concentration of the 'juice' modified. The cultures are sometimes even submitted to a period of fasting. The treatment to be applied differs according to the case, and there are no precise rules. Everything depends on the experience and 'clinical' sense of the operator.

The material organization of a laboratory for tissue-culture is not very complicated. The difficulties which arise can generally be traced to the lack of rigorous care that must be given to the slightest detail and the long experience that is necessary to keep them in good health.

The development of this science depends entirely on the possibility of maintaining the principal types of cells in a state of pure cultures. Carrel has demonstrated that this is possible. The study of these cultures has revealed that each cellular type is characterized not only by its morphological aspect but also by an aggregate of special physiological properties. These properties remained unknown up till now because they were hidden by the tremendous complexity of the phenomena which take place in the organism. It is impossible to know the physiological state of the cells and, consequently, the significance of what is observed, if cells taken from a living animal or an impure culture (mixture of cells of different species) are studied by means of the old techniques as was done and is still done by certain workers. It is only by means of colonies composed of a single-cell type, placed in flasks containing a medium of known composition, and manifesting a measurable form of activity, that it becomes possible to establish a relation between the morphological state (as seen under the microscope) and the functional state of the cells.

The culture of tissues has already considerably increased our knowledge of cell physiology, and we are only at the beginning. For in spite of the fact that this method is already fairly old, there are few scientific centres where it is employed. This is due to the difficulties mentioned above, to the expense involved, and to the fact that, to be fruitful, it requires real talent, great manual dexterity, patience, and imagination.

However, it will certainly be fruitful in the hands of the new generation of biologists.

Besides the fundamental classical problems which can be attacked, this method will certainly reveal, and has already revealed, new problems which otherwise might always have remained ignored. I shall illustrate this statement by two suggestive examples.

We have seen that the fragments of muscular tissue, removed from the heart of a chicken embryo, frequently continue to beat in the culture. Fisher made the following remarkable experiment.

If two palpitating fragments, proceeding from the same heart, are put next to each other, but without touching, one usually observes that their rhythm is not identical. One fragment beats eighty times a minute, for instance, the other fifty. If it so happens, which is rare, that their pulsations are identical, they are nevertheless not synchronous. But these fragments proliferate and gradually surround themselves with a circle of new cells which penetrate into the medium in the shape of a thin, translucid, living layer. After a certain length of time these membranes issued from the two fragments come into contact. At that very moment, *the rhythm becomes identical*. The synchronism is re-established; the two fragments beat as one.

The bird has been long dead; the small pieces of muscle separated from its heart have neither blood circulation nor a nervous system connected to a main trunk, and yet they seem to recognize each other as soon as they come in contact. They persist in accomplishing the work for which their cells were created, not in a haphazard independent fashion but together and co-ordinately. Needless to say, there is not the beginning of an explanation for this curious phenomenon.

Another example: a single isolated cell does not proliferate by mitosis. It cannot reproduce and dies without offspring, even though it appears to be identically in the same conditions as the healthy culture from which it has been separated and the cells of which proliferate rapidly. Cellular growth and multiplication requires the presence of a certain number of cells in the same medium. Everything occurs, in brief, as if certain substances secreted by the cells were required to set free the mechanism of proliferation of the other cells. In other words, they have to be fecundated. What are these substances; what is the mechanism? Can it in some way be compared to a particular form of sexuality, or is this phenomenon connected with the oxidation-reduction potential of the medium? All these problems are still very mysterious.

We have insisted on the necessity of employing pure cultures, composed of a single type of cell. This is a capital point, but also the most delicate of the method. Its importance was not fully realized by many workers who at the start were filled with enthusiasm by the possibilities which they foresaw. Some of them, when they finally understood, were soon discouraged by the meticulous care, the patience, the time, and the technical equipment required to conduct successfully constructive experiments. The tissue-culture laboratory at the Rockefeller Institute comprises about fifteen people: experimenters, assistants, women technicians, and orderlies.

Even though certain species of cells can now be isolated by well-established techniques, there are other varieties which have only been isolated once or twice, thanks to a sequence of circumstances not always reproducible. One or more factors remain undetermined. The general method of selection consists in finding culture media of such composition that they will favour the proliferation of the cells which are to be isolated whilst discouraging the others. Small variations in the concentration of the embryonic juice, addition of blood-serum, and modification in the rhythm of the transplantations are amongst the principal means employed. But there are others, depending on the nature of the cells. Epithelial cells, for instance, live only on condition that they are placed at the surface of the coagulated plasma drop. Naturally it is important to obtain the fragments of tissue from the embryo in as pure a state as possible. This is not always easy. The dissection of a thyroid gland on an eight- or ten-day embryo does not always succeed. It is not exactly child's play to dissect the eye of an embryo in order to secure the pigmented epithelium which surrounds the iris.

Experiments can be conducted only with cultures at least three months old. At that age they constitute relatively homogeneous units. They can then be submitted to different diets so as to permit the study of either their morphological modifications, their physiological reactions, or alterations in their general behaviour and mobility.

These modifications can be reversible as, for instance, alterations of the structures or dimensions of the cells and of their elements, or irreversible, such as the transformation of one type of cell into another. Certain cells develop only in groups and form tissues (fibroblasts, epithelium, etc.). Others, on the contrary, are independent, and manifest a certain individual activity. Leucocytes (white cells) and macrophages are in this category. The latter are found almost everywhere in the organism. In blood, in lymph, in bone marrow, in conjunctive tissue. When cultivated in plasma, macrophages transform themselves into large cells surrounded by an undulating membrane. The addition of certain substances such as aminopeptones, organic enzymes, brings about the disappearance of these membranes and the transformation of the mobile cells into fixed cells. But these changes are reversible. The membranes reappear after a few days in an appropriate medium. On the contrary, when the cells of a culture of macrophages are transformed into fibroblasts by the addition of an extract of Rous sarcoma (spontaneous chicken cancer) the change is irreversible. The same is true of fibroblasts treated with plasma containing heparin (heparin is a substance which keeps plasma from coagulating). The fibroblasts turn into macrophages, acquire all the physiological properties of the latter—mobility and the power of phagocytosis—and conserve them.

A culture does not completely cease growing when it is made to fast. Its life is, however, very much slowed down, as was shown by Fischer. The conditions resemble much more the normal conditions in the organism. But its activity manifests itself in other ways. The cells function physiologically. Instead of proliferating rapidly they accomplish the tasks which they fill in the organism and begin to secrete the substances which they produce normally. In my laboratory at the Pasteur Institute where a pure liver-culture had been isolated (Doljansky) it had been noticed that the well-fed cells no longer manufactured 'glycogene', a substance which transforms itself into sugar (glucose) and is one of the most important products normally elaborated by this organ. When, however, the culture had been submitted to a reduced diet by the suppression of the embryo juice, the glycogenic functions started working again exactly as in the organism. The same phenomenon was observed with the pigment cells of the iris. When too well nourished, the cells proliferate abundantly but without producing any pigment or colouring matter. When dieted, they cease growing in number, but secrete the black pigment which characterizes them *in vivo*.

It is evident that this method is particularly adapted to the study of cancer. It suffices to compare pure cultures proceeding from malignant cells to cells of the same type but devoid of malignancy. It was thus soon ascertained that macrophages proceeding from Rous sarcoma are unhealthy abnormal cells which degenerate rapidly and do not live long. They require the same nourishment as normal macrophages, but unlike the latter they *actively digest the coagulum*. The fibroblasts proceeding from another tumour, the 'Crocker no. 10' are, on the other hand, strong and healthy, require the same nourishment as normal fibroblasts, but *also digest* the coagulum. Epithelial cells from the Ehrlich carcinoma are unhealthy and delicate cells like those of the Rous sarcoma. They *likewise digest* the coagulum.

Other types of malignant cells have been studied, and it was found that no matter how divergent they are on certain points they all have properties in common, such as this faculty of digesting and liquefying the solid part of the coagulum, the fibrin. Furthermore, they can assimilate substances which do not nourish normal cells. It is therefore possible to conclude, as does Dr. Carrel, that cancerous cells acquire their malignancy *in vivo* because of their faculty of manufacturing nutritive substances from the surrounding tissues and fluids. This enables them to proliferate in an unlimited fashion. The mutability of certain types of cells, which we spoke of above, takes on all its importance at this point. Malignant cultures are varieties of normal types from which they differ only slightly through certain properties. These differences are not qualitative but quantitative and irreversible. After several years of culture *in vitro* they have not regressed to the original type. They are fixed varieties.

The hypothesis of the microbic nature of cancer has been definitely abandoned as a result of these experiments and of many others which it would take too long to describe in detail. Unfortunately, the knowledge thus obtained has not yet resulted in any practical progress towards the eradication of this scourge. But these researches have only started and every hope is permissible.

The almost unlimited applications of this method are easy to conceive. Thanks to it we can study the problems of immunity. A tissue behaves like an organism and reacts against the poisoning due to the toxic substances carried by microbes by manufacturing the specific antidote substances called antibodies. From a practical point of view, Carrel and Rivers succeeded in cultivating smallpox vaccine by inoculating it to cultures of cornea, skin, and embryonic tissue. The virus multiplies rapidly, and it is probable that a chicken embryo reduced to a fine pulp can produce as much vaccine as a calf.

The reader had to have precise notions on tissue-culture in general so as to be able to follow the development of the technique employed in checking the method of quantitative study of cicatrization expounded in the preceding chapters. That is why I have kept this problem for the end.

Dr. Carrel was induced to study these problems by former experiments on the ageing of animals. These experiments had led him to admit that with age blood-serum accumulates toxines which are increasingly noxious or abundant. He had convinced himself of this fact by a series of experiments. One of these is particularly striking and deserves to be mentioned, especially as it was never published.

There was at the Rockefeller Institute, before the war, a dog nearly eighteen years old. This poor animal never stirred from its corner and could hardly get up to eat. He slept all day, his coat was coming out, his eyes were dim, and his eyelids stuck together.

This animal was anaesthetized, put on the operating table and treated as follows. Carrel bled him by the carotid artery and removed nearly two-thirds of his blood. This blood was collected aseptically and immediately centrifuged, so as to separate the red cells from the serum. The red cells were washed in Ringer solution, recentrifuged and mixed with fresh Ringer solution to re-establish the initial volume of the blood. This was then re-injected to the dog. The circulation was restored by massaging the heart, and the skin was sewn up. A prince of royal blood, heir to the throne, on whom the peace of the world depended, could not have been the object of more attentive care than this old animal. After several days he had regained strength and appetite. The same operation was repeated so as to eliminate practically all the serum of his blood and replace it by this artificial solution which, besides the blood cells, contained only salts such as chlorides of sodium, potassium, and calcium in the same proportion as those found in the blood. The animal lived. Not only did he live, but, once over the operative shock, he was a different dog. He ran and barked, a thing he had not done for years. His eyes were clear, his eyelids normal. His coat started to come in; he was gay, active, and most important of all, he was no longer indifferent to the charms of the other sex. He was regenerated.

The logical conclusion which Carrel deduced from this remarkable experiment was that his hypothesis on the increase of toxicity of serum with age was verified, and that the symptoms of senescence are the expression of profound physico-chemical and chemical changes occurring in the organism through the influence of time. When the war was over and he had come back to New York he decided to prove this point.

The first experiments simply consisted in cultivating the conjunctive tissue of chick embryo in plasma taken from chickens of different ages. He ascertained that growth was more active in the plasma of young animals than in that of old ones. This fact demonstrated the possibility of employing fibroblast cultures to put in evidence the modifications introduced into the serum by age. The technique was then improved so as to eliminate the most palpable causes of error and to obtain quantitative values.[1] Experiments were performed in the following way: an equal quantity of serum taken from six-week to nine-year-old chickens was added to the culture medium. It was observed that the growth of the cultures was hardly or not at all affected by the serum of a chick six weeks old. Growth was retarded, however, by the addition of serum removed from older animals, and all the more so the older the animal was. Furthermore, under well-determined conditions, the span of life of a culture was affected in the same way. That is to say that, if a culture lived four or six days in the plasma of a nine-year-old cock, it would live forty-six days or more in that of a chick six weeks old. The rate of growth is modified in a similar fashion, and decreases as a function of the age of the animal from which the serum proceeds.

Through further experiments Carrel convinced himself that this retardation was not due to the neutralization of accelerating substances but to the accumulation of toxic products. The curves shown in Figs. 24 and 25 were obtained by taking arbitrarily as base (100 per cent) the rate attained when employing the plasma of three-month-old chickens. This was the age of the animals which furnished

[1] A. Carrel and A. H. Ebeling, *Journ. of Exp. Medicine,* vol. 34, p. 599 (1921).

the plasma in the ordinary technique, and it was therefore of interest to use it. These curves express in percentage the part played by age in the duration of life and in the activity of proliferation.

It can be seen that the drop is much more rapid in the

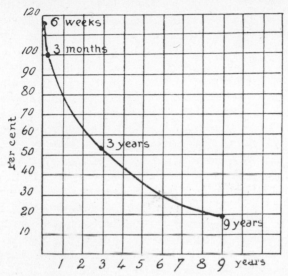

FIG. 24. DURATION OF LIFE 'IN VITRO' OF FIBROBLASTS AS A FUNCTION OF THE AGE OF THE ANIMALS FROM WHICH THE PLASMA WAS TAKEN

first years and especially in the first months. This indicates that the inhibiting power of the plasma increases much more rapidly at the beginning than at the end of life, and tends towards a constant value. If these curves are now compared with that of Fig. 26 representing the variations of the index of cicatrization studied previously, it is obvious that *a striking similarity exists between them*. This last curve represents the evolution of i for a wound of 40 sq. cm.

The growth index which can be deduced from Carrel's experiments is therefore closely related to the index of cicatrization. Both these indices are a measure of the irreversible transformations progressively introduced into an organism by age.

A certain relationship on general lines could evidently be foreseen *a priori*. But nothing authorized the prediction that the differences due to age would be more important at the beginning than at the end of life. In other words, it was in no way evident that the plasma of an animal would reflect

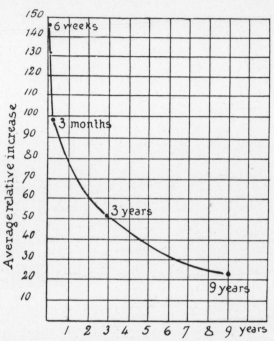

FIG. 25. RATE OF GROWTH OF FIBROBLASTS AS A FUNCTION OF THE AGE OF THE ANIMALS FROM WHICH THE SERUM WAS TAKEN

so exactly the complex variations due to the ageing of a human being.

It is true that many of the characteristics of cicatrization can be found in tissue-cultures. For instance, the considerable acceleration of cellular proliferation brought about by a lesion. Fischer put this phenomenon in evidence by placing cultures under such conditions that their rate of growth became very slow and that they could be maintained for several days without transplanting. He cut out a small square on a relatively large culture the proliferating activity of which was very slow. The proliferation immediately became very active around the wound, which healed rapidly. This proliferation

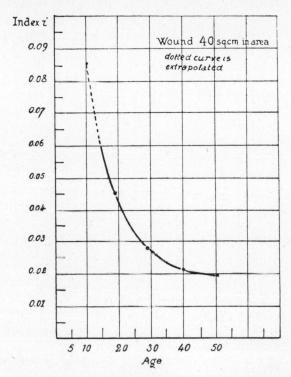

FIG. 26. INDEX OF CICATRIZATION AS A FUNCTION OF THE AGE OF THE PATIENT

ceased as soon as cicatrization was complete. In short, there is an almost absolute identity with the biological phenomenon of cicatrization *in vivo*, and we are faced with the same problems. How is this proliferation started and how is it stopped? This is a most important point, for it is one of the differences between healthy and cancerous tissues. In a cancerous tissue the cells do not receive the order to stop, or if they receive it, they are incapable of obeying.

.   .   .   .   .

Thus, we are in possession of two methods enabling us to study age and the process of ageing. The first *in vivo*, by means of a complete organism, manifesting differences in the rate of reparation at different periods of its evolution. The second *in vitro*, by means of a living reagent which is eternal in comparison with the short duration of our existence and the activity of which is checked proportionally to the *toxic power developed in the serum of a normal animal by the simple fact that it undergoes the limited evolutive cycle* due to its rank in the hierarchy of organized beings. In the first case we observe the result of the accumulation of toxins and of other unknown phenomena on an organism whose entire vital activity is governed by the immutable cycle characterizing our human condition. In the second and much simpler case, we dispose of a living element, artificially removed from the periodical evolution necessary to all organized beings and of which only the constituent parts—the cells—eventually obey the universal law of ageing and death. The tissue-culture does not age and does not die, barring accidents. It has no consciousness comparable to ours. It has no 'individual' existence, and only represents the summation of an infinity of elementary lives. From this angle it is comparable to a species rather than to an individual, for the species persists with all its characteristics and without taking into account the death of its members. And yet if a culture is treated with normal serum from an animal of the same species, its activity is reduced to a value corresponding to the age of this animal. The flow of time has therefore not had the same action on the culture as on the chicken. It affects the first no more than it would an inert body, whereas it inevitably sweeps the bird to its death in obedience to a millennial rhythm. Not only does it affect an organized being from birth, but the *rate* of ageing is different at the beginning and at the end of life and much more rapid during youth.

Consequently, there are two kinds of time. One corresponding to the classical notion, the sideral, physical time, without beginning and without end, flowing in a continuous, uniform, rigid fashion. The other, the physiological time, the duration of our organism, which begins and ends with us, and which does not affect identically in our youth and our old age the phenomena of which we are the seat. It is a time which remembers. It is no longer the impersonal, rigorous time measured by the rotation of the earth, the immutable and arithmetical time in which the universe evolves. Its flow seems to be submitted to periodical fluctuations. It rebounds with each germ: a living time.

But, on the whole, what is time? Is it not absurd to say that it flows? Can we measure physiological time with the same units as the other, the time of inert things? Are they really differentiable? We will now try to study these questions successively.

PART III
TIME

CHAPTER VIII

TIME—DEFINITIONS—MEASUREMENTS

A GREAT deal has been said and written about time. When speaking of it we have been obliged to employ current, ordinary words coined for other purposes. This has resulted in paradoxes, misunderstandings, and endless discussions. The majority of words employed to define an object, a force, or a tendency, necessarily imply the notion of time, for they evoke movements, relations, successions. The verb 'to be', which is indispensable, implies the idea of existence, and the idea of existence imposes the notion of time. All words are therefore inadequate, for one can only define a thing accurately by means of words which do not evoke ideas incorporating the very thing which has to be defined.

We conceive space as something which surrounds us, and time as something which flows beside us and through us. These projections of our thought are at the same time logical and illusory. Ideas on this subject have evolved, however. We shall attempt to explain them.

There are notable analogies and also flagrant differences between space and time. It is impossible to separate these two concepts, for we constantly use one to measure the other. A distance, that is to say, a dimension of space, has a meaning only if a certain time is needed to cover it. If the distance which separates two points could be covered in null time, it would be rigorously equivalent to a definition of a null distance or to the superposition of two points, identical to one. The very existence of matter is inseparable from time by the mere fact that the word 'existence' has been pronounced. *It is impossible to conceive a material object existing instantaneously.*

The certitude that we have of finding it similar to itself after a given time, be it ever so short, gives it what we call its existence, its reality. Just as space marks the coexistence of perceptions at one period of time—we measure the scope of our domain—so time marks the progression of perceptions to a position in space. The combination of these two modes or change of position with change of time is motion, which is the basic condition of our perception.

At first glance it seems, however, that there are certain fundamental differences between space and time. For instance, space, taken as a method of perceiving coexisting objects, according to the idea developed amongst others by Karl Pearson[1] and as a mode of perception enabling us to distinguish groups of immediate sense-impressions, is associated with the world of actual phenomena which we project beyond us. For this reason it has been called a mode of *external* perception.

On the other hand, time is the perception of sequence in the accumulated sense-impressions. It is the relation between past perceptions and present perceptions. Thus, time in its essence, implies memory and thought, or in other words: consciousness. In reality consciousness could be defined as the power to perceive things separately in succession. From this standpoint, time has been called an internal mode of perception. This is in substance Bergson's idea of duration which we will take up again later. A moment's reflection soon shows, however, that this differentiation has no value, for no distinction based on the words 'external' or 'internal' can exist. Indeed, the perceptions of exterior objects can always be traced back to the simple sense-impressions through which we know these objects. It is therefore clear that the arbitrary difference between the exterior and the interior of our ego is nothing but a simple distinction of daily practical convention.

'Take a needle,' says Pearson. 'We say that it is thin, bright, pointed and so forth. What are these properties but a group of sense-impressions relating to form and colour associated with conceptions drawn from past sense-impressions? Their immediate source is the activity of certain optic nerves. These sense-impressions form for us

[1] Pearson, Karl, *The Grammar of Science*, 3rd ed., 1911, London.

the reality of the needle. Nevertheless, they and the resulting construct are projected outside ourselves, *and supposed* to reside in an external thing "the needle". Now, by mischance we run the needle into our finger; another nerve is excited and an unpleasant sense-impression, one which we term painful, arises. This, on the other hand, we term "in ourselves", and do not project into the needle. Yet the colour and form which constitute for us the needle are just as much sense-impressions within us as the pain produced by its prick. The distinction between ourselves and the outside world is thus only an arbitrary, if a practically convenient, division between one type of sense-impression and another. The group of sense-impressions forming what I term *myself* is only a small subdivision of the vast world of sense-impressions.'

Bergson disengaged very clearly the necessary but vague notion of physical time from the more precise notion of duration which had been perceived by other authors and the meaning of which we summarized above. May I here cite a few sentences borrowed from his book *Durée et Simultanéité*,[1] which the reader might have difficulty in finding as the last edition is exhausted.

'How do we pass from this interior time to the time of things? We perceive the material world, and this perception seems to us, rightly, or wrongly, to be at the same time in us and outside us. From one point of view, it is a state of consciousness. From the other it is a superficial film of matter in which the sentient and the sensed would coincide. At every moment of our interior life corresponds a moment of our body and of all surrounding matter which would be simultaneous to it. This matter appears to participate in our conscious duration. Gradually, we extend this duration to the material world as a whole because we do not see any reason for limiting it to the immediate neighbourhood of

[1] Paris, Alcan, 5e édition, 1929.

our body. The universe seems to us to form a whole.
We think that if the part which surrounds us lasts in the
same manner as we do, the same must be true for that which
surrounds this first part, and so on indefinitely. Thus is
born the idea of a duration of the universe, that is to say,
of an impersonal consciousness which would be the connecting link between all the individual ones as well as
between these and the rest of nature. . . .

'Thus our duration and a certain felt and lived participa-
tion of our material environment to this interior duration,
are experimental facts. One cannot speak of a reality which
lasts without introducing consciousness. The metaphysician
will bring into play the direct intervention of a universal
consciousness. The common mortal will only think about
it vaguely. The mathematician will not need to take it
into consideration, for he is interested in the measurement
of things and not in their nature. But should he ask himself
what he measures, and fix his attention on time itself, he
would necessarily visualize succession, and in consequence
the before and the after, and therefore a bridge between
the two (otherwise there would only be one of the two,
a pure instantaneity). Now, we repeat once more, it is
impossible to imagine or to conceive a hyphen between the
before and the after, without an element of memory and,
consequently, of consciousness.

'The use of this word may perhaps repel if an anthropo-
morphic meaning is attached to it. But to visualize a thing
which lasts, it is not necessary to transport into the interior
of the object one's personal memory, even though attenuated.
No matter how much it is diminished in its intensity a
certain amount of the variety and richness of the interior
life would remain there and it would therefore conserve its
personal or, at any rate, human character. We should
consider one moment of the unrolling of the universe, that
is an instantaneity existing independently of all consciousness, then try to evoke conjointly another moment as close
as possible to the first, and thus bring into the world a

minimum of time without allowing the faintest gleam of memory to pass with it. Without an elementary memory linking one instant to another there will only be one or the other of the two, consequently, a unique instant, and no before and after, no succession, no time. This elementary memory can be reduced to only just what is needed to make this link. It can be the link itself, a simple prolongation of the before into the immediate after with a perpetually renewed forgetfulness of what is not the immediate anterior moment. Nevertheless, memory will have been introduced. In truth it is impossible to distinguish between duration, no matter how short, which separates two instants, and a memory which binds them together, for duration is essentially a continuation of what is no more in what is. This is the true time, I mean the time perceived and lived. It is also every kind of conceived time, for it is impossible to conceive time without depicting it as perceived and lived. Duration, then, implies consciousness, and we put consciousness into things by the very fact that we attribute to them a time which lasts.'[1]

One might almost say that these ideas of Bergson are contained implicitly in Descarte's phrase: 'Je pense donc je suis.' ('I think; hence I am.')

Here we have the notion of universal time perfectly defined; for, on the subject of knowing whether the universe is divisible or not into worlds independent one from another, Bergson adds: '. . . If the question had to be resolved we would choose in the actual state of our knowledge, the hypothesis of a material time, *one and universal*.'

But there is another difference between space and time which appears to be fundamental. We can travel in every direction in a three-dimensional space. We can, at will, displace ourselves rapidly or slowly, stay motionless or even come back on our footsteps. The same is not true of time. Not only is it impossible to remain motionless, but one cannot

[1] *Durée et Simultanéité*, 5e édition, p. 60 and following.

travel backwards in it, and no one can boast of being able to regulate its rate of flow. 'It does not cease,' says Sir James Jeans, 'to unfold itself at a uniform and uncontrollable rate which is the same for each one of us.' What is the significance of this difference between space and time?

It is probably solely due to a misunderstanding, to a faulty symbolical representation of relatively clear notions.[1] Indeed, in effectuating any kind of a displacement, the first condition to be fulfilled is to exist; in other words, if a conscious being is concerned, to begin to register an evolution through memory. The very distance which has to be covered exists only at the moment when it is covered—no matter in which way, materially or conceptually—and by the very fact that it is covered. It may be objected that it suffices to conceive it for it to exist. But a moment's reflection shows that there is a gulf between a concept and a reality. The proof being that we can easily conceive or imagine things which we know to be impossible, for instance, the cessation of the flow of time or its inverted flow. The important thing for us is *reality*. It may also be objected that to separate two points A and B in space, it suffices to see a distance without having to cover it ourselves. But our notion of distance between A and B, no matter how short it is, implies that it exists in time, and it exists for us only from the moment when we have seen it. Hence I take the word 'cover' in the very broad sense of perceiving, for the simple fact of perceiving two points even simultaneously, implies that it would take a certain time to go from one to another. No distance exists, and naturally no displacement can be executed outside of time. We have points of reference in space, systems of reference such as the three axes of co-ordinates, for instance, thanks to which we know that we

---

[1] I have already spoken of the fact that we are forced to employ words that have been coined for our current thoughts and daily life. This makes it very difficult to express relations which we seize intuitively and which we must translate in a language necessarily inadequate. It is certain that a great number of discussions and divergencies of opinion are due to this state of things. It is as if one tried to construct a flower with a puzzle representing a locomotive.

are going in a certain direction or coming back on our steps. There is nothing similar in time. Time is the *very condition* of the existence of the three directions of space, which, we repeat, begin to exist for us only from the moment we see them. If we cover a distance in a certain direction, stop and then come back on our footsteps, we have in all evidence evolved in time. But time, which is concreted by the succession of our states of consciousness, cannot distinguish between the different directions which we have taken. We say that it has been simply unrolled, and we mean by this that we have lasted. It is therefore absurd to try to compare time and space, for space *has no significance for us outside of time*. It is as absurd as trying to compare the wavelength 0·589 μ to yellow light. The colour or impression which we translate by the word 'yellow' and which has a very definite meaning for us, exists only if an electromagnetic radiation of a wavelength equal to 0·589 μ is intercepted on its path by a human eye. The same is true of a rainbow, so clearly seen and which we carry with us in the rain. In reality it exists, as we see it, only at the back of our eye. We carry our time with us, and it is through its intermediary that we construct universe and space. A traveller in time, in a remarkable story by H. G. Wells says: 'There is no difference between Time and any of the three dimensions of Space, except that our consciousness moves along it.' (*The Time Machine.*) In citing this phrase Silberstein,[1] one of the first commentators on the theory of relativity, stated that Wells had thus marvellously anticipated this theory.

The preceding lines have been written with the aim of preparing the reader to accept the modern conception deduced by Minkowski from the first works of Einstein. This concept is based on altogether different reasoning, but also results in the intimate fusion of time and space. It is admitted that matter is electric in its structure, so that all physical and chemical phenomena are, in the last resort, electrical phenomena. Minkowski demonstrated that the theory of relativity requires

[1] Silberstein, *The Theory of Relativity.* London, 1914, p. 134.

that all electric phenomena be considered as taking place, not in separate time and space, as had been thought so far, but in a space and time welded together so intimately that, following Sir James Jeans' expression, it is impossible to separate space from time in any absolute manner. None of the phenomena of nature is capable of dissociating the result into a separate space and time.

There is nothing in this statement to astonish the reader if he has followed the preceding paragraphs. On the contrary, a different conclusion would surprise him if he has thoroughly grasped Bergson's and Pearson's notion of duration in which consciousness necessarily intervenes, and also the simple elementary fact that nothing can exist instantaneously, seeing that the verb 'to exist' in itself implies the notion of time. If the reader is thoroughly impregnated by these purely logical ideas, he will not be able to conceive how it is possible to think otherwise. As a result, the notion of time as *a fourth dimension* not of space, as has often erroneously been said, but of the universe, imposes itself as being not only plausible but necessary.[1]

I must say that I cannot see any difficulty in conceiving what Minkowski calls 'the four-dimensional continuum'. The perusal of works such as those of Eddington, Jeans, and Bergson's *Durée et Simultanéité*, give the impression that it requires a kind of intellectual feat.

'It is difficult to imagine a new dimension if one starts from three-dimensional space,' writes Bergson, 'seeing that experience does not show us a fourth one. . . .'

'It is difficult enough to imagine the four-dimensional continuum. . . .' writes Sir James Jeans.

I wonder if this is not another snare set for us by 'words'. In other terms is it not principally the word 'dimension' which makes things difficult? For if we persist in trying to imagine a supernumerary dimension of space we cannot help considering it as being of the same order, of the same nature

---

[1] In the *Encyclopedia* of 1754, d'Alembert had foreseen this conception, or more exactly had mentioned '*a clever man of his acquaintance who believes that time could be considered as a fourth dimension*'.

as the others: it bears the same name. Now, if the three dimensions are *necessary* for the conception of all the directions in space, they are also *sufficient* to account for our material universe, and there is no place for the intruder in the familiar trihedron of Euclidean space. As the dimensions of space are schematized by three straight lines converging rectangularly the layman tries to figure the 'fourth' in spite of himself as another 'direction'. At any rate this is the impression I received when talking to most people. And this notion is absolutely erroneous. The fourth dimension, as stated above, only represents the *existence* of the three others, the existence of the trihedron or any other system of reference. It simply indicates *the birth* in our consciousness of the notion of the three-dimensional space. The history of material points, whether stationary or not, in the system of reference determined by our three rectangular co-ordinates begins the moment this birth has taken place. The phenomena have a point of departure; they evolve; our senses and our memory register them and draw conclusions and laws from them. They are alive for us. Suppress time and nothing remains. The antithesis can be found in Herodotus: 'Let time be lavished and all that is possible will come to pass.' The theory of probability gives this sentence a profound meaning.

Minkowski's own words: 'Space and time considered in themselves and individually must henceforth retire into the shade, and only a kind of combination of the two must keep a certain reality', do not sufficiently bring out the fact that *all reality is the direct consequence of the conjugation of space and time.* The physicist does not have the same difficulty in conceiving the fourth dimension, perhaps because of the habit he has of giving a much broader meaning to the word 'dimension'. He reduces the quantities which he measures to three units: centimetre, gram, second, with which he can describe his universe. But the C.G.S. system comprises precisely the four dimensions and, in addition, a more complex dimension of mass. The physicist brings the most diverse magnitudes back to these three basic units and establishes dimensional formulae in which the fundamental dimensions are fused into a single magnitude endowed with different material properties. For example, he expresses the unit of volume by L^3, seeing that the measurement of a volume is obtained by multiplying three lengths one by the other. For the unit, these lengths are equal and give $L \times L \times L = L^3$.

He likewise expresses the unit of velocity by $\dfrac{L}{T}$ or LT^{-1}, since velocity is length divided by time. Acceleration, which is the quotient of velocity by time becomes LT^{-2}. But with the same symbols he can write the formulae of very complex units such as that of quantity of electricity: $L^{\frac{3}{2}}M^{\frac{1}{2}}T^{-1}$ of potential difference: $L^{\frac{3}{2}}M^{\frac{1}{2}}T^{-2}$ of magnetic moment $L^{\frac{5}{2}}M^{\frac{1}{2}}T^{-1}$ or simply that of work or of moment of force: L^2MT^{-2}. Absolute notions, such as that of energy, are naturally beyond the scope of these definitions. Thus, the physicist, accustomed as he is to juggling with various dimensions, escapes the temptation of comparing them to each other except to bring them back to conventional units. For instance, he will say that a magnitude 'has the dimensions of a velocity'. This is a stenographic expression which simply means that time enters into the formula as a denominator. If he speaks of 'the dimensions of an acceleration' it means that time is to be found as a denominator but at the power 2.

Though everybody is aware of the fact that in order to measure time one must resort to the displacement of an object in space, we will develop this subject a little further. If we perceived only two dimensions instead of three, it would be almost impossible to assure oneself that time flows uniformly. Indeed, let us suppose that a distant mobile body travels along a path in the plane of our vision. Let us suppose, for example, that we are examining the movement of a body on the earth from a great height, say from the moon. If this body—a marble, for instance—covers equal distances in equal times, we cannot infer that its movement is uniform, for by definition, we have no means of knowing if the ground on which the marble rolls is rigorously plane. Should this not be the case, if there are hollows and bumps, ascents and descents, we cannot speak of equal distances as we do not know the value of the angles of the route in the plane of observation. A yardstick appears to be only 3·6 inches long if looked at from a certain angle. In this case, if an ant takes two minutes to go from one end to another of this yardstick we will be under the impression that it has taken two minutes to cover 3·6 inches, that is at a rate ten times slower than the reality. Let us take another illustration. An observer on the moon seeing a scenic railway on earth as a simple railroad could not explain the variations of speed observed even if the cars were propelled by a motor imparting a uniform velocity to them. He can only see the projection of the undulated track on the ground, the trace of his plane of vision. In order to detect the undulations he would have to look sidewise, namely to move in the third dimension. One can conceive that it would be easy to give this observer the impression that the speed is uniform by imparting to the wagon, by means of a motor, such speeds as to make up for the apparent slowing up due to the descents and ascents. The three dimensions are thus necessary to allow the measurement of time just as time is necessary for the perception of dimensions; that is to say, of matter.

I trust that the notion of the 'four-dimensional continuum' is now clear in the mind of the reader. In all the formulae of Relativity the fourth dimension is not expressed by the symbol of time, t, but by another, proportional to it, obtained by multiplying t, for practical reasons which I cannot explain here, by the square root of -1 $(ct\sqrt{-1})$; that is by the symbol of the 'imaginary' numbers.[1]

If the idea of the four-dimensional continuum, our universe,

[1] The symbol t introduced by Minkowski does not express time in current units, that is to say, in seconds, but in units represented by the reciprocal of the velocity of light. These mathematical expedients, by which it was possible to materialize Minkowski's conception, have given it all its value. We are reminded by Houllevigue (*Revue de Paris*, April 15th 1935) that Pflüger when mentioning this discovery said, 'One must be a mathematician to appreciate fully the aesthetic joy given by this conception.'

is clear, that of a *deformed* continuum is less so. And yet the *general* theory of Relativity explains gravitation by a deformation of the continuum. The existence of a 'force' which acts in inverse ratio to the square root of the distance and deflects the normally rectilinear course of bodies in space, is admitted in the classical theory of Newton. But the theory of Relativity does not accept mysterious 'unknowable' forces.[1] The formulae which define its continuum, based, it is true, on a certain number of undemonstrated postulates, must explain everything. From the relativistic point of view, the criticism of Newton's theory can be summarily expressed in the following fashion. This theory is based on a hypothetical motion never observed by any one: the straight-line motion, arbitrarily named natural motion. To explain all natural motions we have to bring into play unknown forces the existence of which can only be proved by the hypothesis from which we started and which cannot be verified. In all evidence we are facing a *petitio principii*. A straight line exists as a geometrical concept, but motion in a straight line does not exist as an objective reality, or at any rate it has never been observed. What I mean is, that if we trace a straight line on paper with a ruler, we have before our eyes a picture which concretes our concept of a straight line, providing that all its points are simultaneously perceived by the eye. But the course of the pencil which has traced this line is far from having been a straight line in the universe. Our hand participated in the complex movements of the earth around its axis, of the earth around the sun, and of the entire solar system in space. The trajectory, as seen by an observer in Sirius, would have been very complicated indeed. It was only in relation to ourselves that it was in a straight line. Thus, when Newton says

[1] We can easily imagine in a one-dimensional space (straight line) the apparition of a force as a simple consequence of a curve (second dimension). For example, the 'centrifugal force' which throws the passengers of an automobile towards the exterior as soon as it abandons a straight line to take a curve (P. Martignan). The single presence of matter deforms the space-time continuum and the force of gravitation is the result. We will take up again this question of deformations a little farther on.

'A body in motion which is not influenced by any force travels in a straight line and its velocity is invariable. Therefore planets follow a curved trajectory because they are continually deviated from their course by forces which act upon them', Einstein simply answers: 'Planets follow their orbits not because they are deviated from their course, but because SUCH IS THEIR NATURAL COURSE.'

What, then, becomes of the straight-line motion? 'The straight-line motion,' answers Einstein, 'is possible only in a Euclidean space; we have never observed it.' We must then admit that our universe is not Euclidean; it is a curved space-time continuum.

The important point which must be grasped here is that this reasoning makes sense only if, as I explained above, the intimate welding of time and space is conceived. If all idea of motion and time could be suppressed, Euclidean space could easily be conceived. But there exists an unbridgeable chasm between this pure, abstract, static geometrical concept and our universe which is essentially 'motion'. It is the chasm which separates the pure idea from reality. All the obscurities invoked, the revolt and the repugnance which have been expressed on the subject of Relativity derive, I think, from our old habit of separating time and space. The idea must become well rooted in our minds that this is an unconscious metaphysical reasoning, whereas Relativity brings us down to earth, face to face with the real, tangible universe. It is above all a practical theory.

This does not mean that the theory itself is true in all its details, nor that it will remain immutable. It never had this pretension. It will evolve, be transformed and adapted to new facts. This is the role of a hypothesis. But it has given us a certain number of new concepts which have made it possible to interpret with greater precision an important number of phenomena. Above all, it has renewed our way of thinking, cleared up many obscurities (has it not suppressed that paradoxical and disturbing entity, Ether?) and steered the science of our epoch in a fruitful direction.

Before passing on to the measurement of time let us come back for an instant to the notion of the deformed—curved—space-time continuum. It is impossible to have a clear picture of this if one considers the three-dimensional space. But a sufficiently close if not absolutely rigorous analogy can be drawn from the idea of a two-dimensional space which we used to show the necessity of the third dimension in the measurement of time. Indeed, time is measured by means of the movement of a mobile body in space. It cannot be measured without displacement. The reader may remember that in the example of a scenic railway mentioned above, we came to the conclusion that the observer in the moon, ignoring the existence of the third dimension which would alone enable him to ascertain that the wagon ascends and descends, could only conceive the acceleration and slowing up observed as being due to variations in the actual velocity of the moving body. On the other hand, if the rate of the moving body was variable as a function of the slope, so that the distance travelled *in projection* was always the same in equal times, the observer would have the impression of a uniform velocity. Thus, curvatures in a path contained in the plane of observation, in a two-dimensional space, would entail gross errors in the determination of the fourth dimension, time. And reciprocally, fluctuations in speed, the cause of which are unknown, would entail errors in the estimation of the distance travelled; that is to say, of space. I repeat once more that this is only an analogy, but it seems to me that this rough comparison enables one to grasp how the deformations of space can affect the measurement of time and how the deformations or variations of velocity, which are the only magnitude at our disposal for measuring time, affect space.

If I have insisted at length on this point, it is because we shall soon see that there is perhaps another means of measuring our time which escapes the causes of error just enumerated.

·   ·   ·   ·

How do we measure time?

'Fortunately for us,' says Karl Pearson, 'we are not compelled to measure it by a description of the sequence of our states of consciousness. There are certain sense-impressions which in our experience repeat themselves identical to themselves, and which correspond, on an average, to the same routine of consciousness. In the first instance, the alternation of night and day has been employed since the first ages of the history of man to register approximately the same sequence of sense-impressions. A day and a night became the measurement of a certain interval of consciousness. We feel but cannot prove that the same amount of states of consciousness can be approximately contained for a normal human being in each interval of a day and a night. It is a matter of experience rather than a demonstrated fact.

'Many identical things happen at intervals of identical time,' continues Pearson, from whom we will borrow the following exceptionally clear lines. 'When we say it is four hours since breakfast, we mean in the first place that the large hand of our clock or watch has gone round the dial four times, a repeated sense-impression which we could, if we please, have observed. But how shall we decide whether each of these four hours represents equal amounts of consciousness, and the same amount to-day as yesterday? It may possibly be that our time-keeper has been compared with a standard clock regulated perhaps from Greenwich Observatory. But what regulates the Greenwich clock? Briefly, without entering into details, it is ultimately regulated by the motion of the earth around the sun. Assuming, however, as a result of astronomical experience, that the intervals day and year have a constant relation, we can throw back the regulation of our clock on the motion of the earth about its axis. We may regulate what is termed the "mean solar time" of an ordinary clock by "astronomical time" of which the day corresponds to a complete turn of the earth on its axis. Now if an observer watches a so-called circumpolar star, or one that remains all day and night above the horizon, it will appear, like the end of his astronomical clock-hand, to describe a circle; the star ought to appear to the observer to describe equal parts of its circle in equal times by his clock, or while the end of the clock-hand describes equal parts of its circle. In this manner the hours on the Greenwich astronomical clock, and ultimately on all ordinary watches and clocks regulated by it, will correspond to the earth turning through equal angles on its axis. We thus throw back our measurement of time on the earth which is taken as a time-keeper. *We admit that equal rotations correspond to equal intervals of conscience.* But all clocks being set by the earth, how shall we be certain that the earth itself is a regular time-keeper? If the earth were gradually to turn more slowly upon its axis, how should we know it was losing time, and how measure the amount? It might be replied that we should find that the year had fewer days in it. But then, how could we settle that it was the day that was growing longer and not the year that was growing shorter. Again, it may be objected that we know a great number of astronomical periods relating to the motion of the planets expressed in terms of days, and that we should be able to tell by comparison with these periods. To this we must answer that the relation of these periods expressed in days and in terms of each other, appears now indeed invariable. But what if all these relations are found to have slightly changed a thousand years hence? Which body shall we say has been moving uniformly? Which bodies have been gaining or losing? Or, what if the ratios of their periods remaining the same, they were all to have lost or gained? How shall we, with such a possibility in view, assert that the hour to-day is the "same interval" as it was a thousand or perhaps a million years back? Now, certain investigations with regard to the frictional action of the tides make it highly probable that the earth is not a perfect time-keeper nor are we able to postulate that regularity of motion by

which alone we could reach absolute time, of any body in
our perceptual experience.

'Astronomy says it is not in me, nor do we get a more
definite answer from physics. Suppose an observer to
measure the distance traversed by light in one second? Is
this at all times a fixed standard of the length of a second?
A thousand years later another observer again measures the
distance for one of *his* seconds and finds it differs from the
old determination. What shall he infer? Is the speed of
light really variable, has the planetary system reached a
denser portion of the ether, has the second changed its
value, or does the fault lie with one or other observer? No
more than the astronomer can the physicist provide us
with an *absolute* measure of time. So soon as we grasp
this, we appear to lose our hold on time. The earth, the
sole clock by which we can measure millions of years, fails
us when we once doubt its regularity. Why should a year
now represent the same amount of consciousness as it
might have done a few million years back? The absolutely
uniform motion by which alone we could reach an absolute
measurement of time, fails us in perceptual experience. It
is, like the geometrical surface, reached in conception and
in conception only, by carrying to a limit there the approximate sameness and uniformity which we observe in certain
perceptual movements.'

Newton, when defining what Pearson will later on call
'conceptual time', thus expresses himself:

'That absolute, true, and mathematical time is conceived
as flowing at a constant rate, unaffected by the speed or
slowness of the motions of material things.'

Clearly, such a time is a pure ideal, for how can we measure
it if there be nothing in the sphere of our perception which
we are certain flows at a constant rate? 'Uniform flow', like
any other scientific concept, is an ideal limit drawn from the

actual acceleration or slowing up of the motions of material things. But, like other scientific concepts, it is invaluable as a shorthand method of description. Perceptual time is the pure order of succession of our sense-impressions and involves no idea of absolute interval. Conceptual time is like a piece of blank paper ruled with equidistant lines upon which we may inscribe the sequence of our perceptions; both the known sequence of the past and the predicted sequence of the future. The fact that, upon the ruled lines, we have inscribed some standard recurring sense-impression (as the daily transit of a heavenly body over the meridian of Greenwich), must not be taken as signifying that states of consciousness succeed each other uniformly or that a 'uniform flow' of consciousness is in some way a measure of absolute time. It denotes no more than this: that from noon to noon the average human being experiences much the same sequence of sense-impressions and that the *same space* in our conceptual time-log may be conveniently allotted for their inscription.

.   .   .   .   .

How does life fit into the preceding theories? Can all the very special phenomena which characterize living beings be assimilated to the phenomena of inorganized matter? Is there not a difference between this physical world and the beings who evolve between birth and death according to a hereditary rhythm, and recommence their ancestral cycle indefinitely? Does not this fact alone introduce something special into this consciousness without which, by definition, the very notion of duration would not exist? It may be objected that we have no proof that the mineral, inorganized world does not also evolve according to a cycle imperceptible only by reason of its tremendous duration. If this period were only of a hundred million years it would entirely escape the scope of our intelligence, and it could be far greater than that. In favour of this theory, we might say that the evolution of our universe is proved by the notion of entropy, a magnitude which grows indefinitely. I will not enter into a discussion which even though interesting would certainly be vain, but will restrict myself to reminding the reader that, in respect to ourselves, to the ephemeral duration of our existence, the difference between the rates of evolution, admitting that this difference exists, would by its colossal size in itself suffice to introduce fundamental differences in the phenomena observed. Indeed, it is known that a great number of the physical properties of matter are determined by the speed of the objects. For instance, by the velocity of the electrons or of the molecules. Mass itself, a basic quality of matter, is a function of velocity. If electrons, or any other projectile, could attain the velocity of light, their mass would become infinite. These are not simple views of the mind, but result from experiments made, amongst others, by Kaufman in 1901 and by Bucherer more than twenty years ago, in which they studied quantitatively the variations of the mass of the electron as a function of its velocity. At our scale, it is a well-known fact that there is a big difference if we are hit by a bullet having a velocity of one metre per second or by one travelling at six hundred metres a second. A spout of water a few centimetres in diameter falling from the height of the Eiffel Tower has the rigidity of an iron bar and cannot be cut by the stroke of a sword.

We are therefore authorized to think that, from the point of view of our senses and of our consciousness, things can be different according to whether the cycle of existence is longer or shorter and according to whether the rhythm of the reactions is more or less accelerated. For a given species, the persistence of life is a discontinuous phenomenon. The individual, like a rocket tracing its luminous trajectory in space, gives birth to another individual, just as if the rocket on coming back to earth put fire to another rocket and so on.[1] This sequence of

---

[1] 'Life appears like a current which goes from germ to germ by the intermediary of a developed organism' (Bergson). We do not know, but it is perhaps the current alone which counts in the history of the universe. For man, on the contrary, it is the intermediary which counts, and the integral phenomenon of which he is only an element escapes him.

brilliant parabolas traced by the rockets themselves at varying velocities, rapidly at the start, when rising, then more slowly as they near their apogee, is only perceived by us, thanks to our eyes and to our memory. We only see it *behind* the rocket, as it rises in darkness. Just as for a living being, we perceive its past but not its future. But we can calculate the latter with fairly great precision. Our observer in the moon, even though he possessed powerful means of observation, would see only the trace of these brilliant trajectories, and if thousands of rockets were disposed in a straight line so that each one in falling put fire to another, he would be under the impression that the *same* little luminous line was advancing slowly on the surface of our globe. The distance would be too great, and the rockets too close to each other for him to be able to perceive the variations of speed. The latter would appear uniform.

This picture applies in a certain measure to life, to the species which perpetuates itself almost uniformly by means of individuals of limited duration. Practically speaking, the time of the species represents an immortality based on mortality. It is the envelope curve of elementary phenomena. But all consciousness is contained in this elementary phenomenon and, as I said above, nothing proves that the 'flow of consciousness', or what amounts to the same thing, the perception of time, is in all consciences and at *every* moment of their *individual cycle*, directly proportional to the physical time, the uniform flow of which is purely conceptual and independent of the life of the individual.

According to Bergson, living matter represents 'a system of growth comparable to an avalanche, where there is no repetition, but where each step forward is a creation, a manifestation of liberty. The living organism is then a reality which creates itself; inorganic matter, on the contrary, is a reality which destroys itself.' (Creative Evolution.)

From whatever angle we look at it, on condition that we are of good faith, we are led to the conclusion that it would be interesting to borrow solely from a living organism the units which are used to define it.

CHAPTER IX

THE TIME OF ORGANIZED BEINGS—
THE CHEMICAL CLOCK

THE visual impression obtained by the observer in the moon mentioned in the preceding chapter, gives rise in his mind to an idea of continuity. This continuity which, neglecting the individual, uniformly pursues its course, would be for us the expression of immortality, or the prolongation beyond death of the individual, and through him, of the characteristics which he had himself inherited from his parents. No matter what mechanisms (sexual or asexual reproduction) are brought into play by nature to impart this immortality, we know that it exists; we can control it. Woodruff, Metalnikov and others have shown that, with unicellular animals (infusoria) one could start with a single individual which spontaneously divides itself in two, then in four and so on, and obtain on an average from six to seven hundred generations a year (about 1·74 generations per day). The experiments were followed for several years (seven years by Woodruff and more than twenty-three years by Metalnikov). It is evidently impossible to speak of the absolute immortality of the cell on the basis of experiments having lasted only a few years. But the idea in itself has become commonplace since the works of Pasteur and the failure of all attempts to create living matter from inorganic matter. To-day as formerly we admit that: '*Omnis cellula a cellula.*' The important fact from our point of view is relative immortality, that is, with respect to the duration of the mean individual cycle, between two cellular divisions or between two births. In unicellular animals the cells do not die—except accidentally—as each one at a given time divides itself in two and starts off again. In superior organisms, the immortal cells are the sexual cells. All the others grow old and die, following a determined rhythm. But the gametes, or sexual cells, are the origin of every organized being which always proceeds from an egg—the female cell—fecundated by the male cell. This fecundated egg develops, and at a certain moment of its evolution becomes an adult organism. This organism manufactures gametes, male or female according to its own sex, and these gametes will in their turn originate identical new organisms. The being which created them will continue its cycle and die. But a part of it will remain, the sexual cell which it has put forth and which alone indefinitely perpetuates the species. Everything therefore occurs as if an organism was nothing but the momentary and mortal intermediary by means of which life can pass from one germ to another, as Bergson expresses it. It is in this sense that we said that sexual cells were immortal.

We have, nevertheless, seen that it was possible, under certain conditions, to assure eternal life, or at any rate a much longer span of existence than is normal, to cells of vertebrates such as birds. It was even shown that these cells do not age. In this case it is difficult to speak of individual consciousness. One can at the most speak of a 'chemical memory'. The word 'memory' is here taken in a very special sense, for it is possible to immunize these cells against certain substances.[1] But, strangely enough, several authors, and amongst others Jennings, Day, and Bertlay in America, have independently observed disturbing facts tending to prove that the *paramecia*, microscopic infusoria, are endowed with real memory, or in other words, that these unicellular beings can profit from their past experience. This would indicate the existence of some kind of consciousness. The study of these problems is fascinating, and Metalnikov has written a remarkable book on this subject which should be read.[2]

Now, from the point of view which concerns us, if life is inherited with its specific characteristics for each species, the same is not true of consciousness. Each birth marks a beginning, and each being who begins to live, or what amounts to

[1] 'The cellular element when energetically solicited keeps the memory of its reaction for a long time' (Bordet).

[2] S. Metalnikov, *Immortalité et Rajeunissement dans la Biologie moderne*. Flammarion, 1924.

the same, to age, must learn anew what his parents learned before him. It is the rocket which rises only to fall again. The individual, therefore, evolves in a personal time which has a beginning and an end. But the time of the species to which he belongs, the 'wave front' time, has practically no beginning and no end. As we have already stated, it is a concept which can have no real value for any of us, any more than the concept of the uniform flow of physical time. The only time which counts for man is his own time, the time which extends between a cradle and a tomb.

We can attain this physiological time directly by means of the two methods described in this book. The method based on the cicatrization of wounds and that based on tissue-cultures. We have already seen that it was possible thus to obtain a measurement of the real physiological age. We shall now see how a measurement of time can be derived from it.

.   .   .   .   .

The reader may remember that we obtained an index of cicatrization i from the rate of cicatrization of the surface wounds. The following pages will show why we insisted at length on the value of this coefficient, the discovery of which was of greater scientific interest than the simple fact that it enabled us to calculate from beginning to end the successive dimensions of a wound. Thanks to it we could for the first time, as was pointed out by Carrel in his admirable book, *Man, the Unknown*, measure the flow of physiological time.

Now, the value of this index (see page 79 et al.) depends both on the area and on the age of the patient. It is all the higher the smaller is the wound and the younger is the man. It was therefore important to eliminate the part played by the area and to find a new coefficient, independent of the dimensions of the wound and truly expressing the physiological activity characteristic of a given age.

The study of a large number of experimental figures showed the possibility of obtaining such a coefficient as well as the limits between which it would be applicable. So as to enable the reader to follow up to the very end in all their details the successive steps of reasoning and thoroughly to understand the way in which the results were obtained, I shall once more take him behind the scenes. He will thus appreciate the extreme simplicity of the method. Let us examine the following table:

CONSTANT OF PHYSIOLOGICAL ACTIVITY A

For the age of twenty

1	2	3	4	5
S Area of the wound in sq. cm.	$\sqrt{S}$	$\dfrac{1}{\sqrt{S}}$	Index i (20 years)	$A_{20}= i\sqrt{S}$
150	12·2	0·081	0·0200	0·244
140	11·8	0·085	0·0210	0·248
130	11·4	0·088	0·0220	0·251
120	10·9	0·091	0·0225	0·245
110	10·5	0·095	0·0240	0·252
100	10·0	0·100	0·0250	0·250
90	9·5	0·106	0·0275	0·252
80	8·95	0·112	0·0300	0·268
70	8·35	0·120	0·0325	0·270
60	7·75	0·129	0·0355	0·274
50	7·06	0·142	0·0400	0·282
40	6·34	0·158	0·0445	0·282
30	5·48	0·182	0·0500	0·274
25	5·00	0·200	0·0540	0·274
20	4·46	0·224	0·0580	0·259
15	3·87	0·258	0·0645	0·250
10	3·16	0·316	0·0700	0·222

Mean value .... $A_{20}=0·260$

Here we have five columns of figures. The first column expresses the areas of the wounds. The second, the values of the square roots of the figures in the first column. The third, the reciprocal value of the figures of the second. The fourth, the values of the index of cicatrization corresponding to each dimension of a wound for the age of twenty. And finally the fifth, the quotient of the figures of the fourth column (index i) by the corresponding figures of the third or, what amounts exactly to the same thing, the values of the product of i by the figures of the second column (square roots).

Why these figures? For the following reasons: As the area decreases the index of cicatrization increases. But the area decreases more rapidly than the index increases. This is obvious: we see in the table that when the area diminishes by one half, from 140 to 70 sq. cm. for instance, the index only increases from 0·210 to 0·0325. When the wound is reduced to one third of its size (from 150 sq. cm. to 50 sq. cm.) the index has only just doubled (from 0·020 to 0·040). It is precisely this absence of proportionality which makes it necessary to take the area into account. But when a quantity decreases, its reciprocal increases. Consequently, when one considers the reciprocal of the area, it varies in the same direction as the index but always with greater rapidity. The aim being to obtain a constant, for then the area could be eliminated, it behoved us to try to see if a quantity did not exist which would be a simple function of the area, and the variations of which would follow as closely as possible the variations of the reciprocal of the index. Now it may be remembered that in establishing the formula, I took only the area into account, except in the case of long, narrow wounds where the role of the epithelial edge is preponderant. In this case, we have seen that the experimental facts could be quantitatively expressed by introducing the square root of the area multiplied by a certain coefficient. It is known that the square root of a square area expresses quantitatively the length of one of the sides. For a square, the product $4 \times \sqrt{S}$ is therefore equal to the length of the sum of the four sides. If the figure is not a square the coefficient 4 alone changes. If the figure contracts, if its area decreases without the shape being altered, the formula $K \times \sqrt{S}$ will always express the length of the sides. On the other hand, we also know that, if the area of a figure decreases, the length of the sides of the outline also decreases, but less rapidly. The relation of the two figures expressing length and area is that of a number to its square.

The idea which immediately imposed itself was to calculate the square roots of the areas and to take their reciprocals (3rd column) so as to see if by chance the increase of i was not proportional to these reciprocals. Now, at first sight, this is actually what happens. Let us take at random a figure in column 3. For example, 0·1 and 0·2, its double in value. We see that the corresponding indices are respectively 0·0250 and 0·0540, a little more than double (ratio exactly equal to 2·15). Let us now take two values of the index, the ratio of which is approximately three: 0·0210 and 0·0645 (ratio equal to 3·07). The corresponding values in the third column are 0·085 and 0·258: the second figure is very nearly treble of the first (ratio equal to 3·04).

From then on the problem was practically solved. As the indices seem to vary proportionally to the reciprocals of the square root of the areas, it suffices to multiply i by $\sqrt{S}$ to obtain a constant factor, the increase of one being exactly balanced by the decrease of the other. This amounts to saying that the area no longer intervenes in this quantity, which will be solely determined by the age of the patient. It is the solution of the problem which we had propounded.

The new coefficient thus calculated, and which shall be designated by the letter A, can then be considered as the coefficient or constant of physiological activity of reparation for a given age, and can be written in the following manner:

$$A = i\sqrt{S}$$

The fifth column of the table on page 148 gives the values of this coefficient. It can be seen at a glance that they are only approximately constant. They vary between 0·24 and 0·22 at the beginning and the end and go up to values attaining 0·28. Does this mean that this coefficient is not sufficiently stable, and that we rejoiced prematurely? It suffices to reflect on the manner in which it is calculated to understand that the reason for these fluctuations lies not so much in an error of reasoning as in the method employed to calculate the values of i. Indeed, these values are obtained from table, p. 85. Most of them are interpolated, and even though the experimental values of i are established on a fairly large number of experiments (about six hundred), it is impossible to affirm that all these values are rigorously exact. Ten thousand experiments would be needed in order to consider the mean values as being really representative. We stated above that the individual differences due to the state of health, to the physiological age, were at first glance negligible, with the exception of certain special cases such as syphilis, diabetes, alcoholism. But it is probable that they nevertheless exist, and that the indices drawn from the chart (p. 87) are only the approximate expression of the true index. Furthermore, differences can exist according to the part of the body on which the wound is located, when the granular contraction depending on the elasticity of the subjacent conjunctive tissue is less efficient. For example, wounds on the skull, on the antero-internal part of the leg (on the tibia), those on the foot or the back of the hand, are characterized by a lower index, owing to the fact that the skin lies almost directly on the bone. Not only is the contraction weaker in these wounds, but blood irrigation through the conjunctive tissue is diminished and can even be null if the bone is bared. All these causes of error introduce small variations in the calculation, but can be easily taken into account by slightly correcting the index if one wishes to establish the curve of a particular wound.

We can, moreover, assure ourselves that the variations of A are due to fluctuations of a negligible magnitude in the values of i. From a practical point of view, only the two first characteristic figures of the values of i are significant, and it can be said that a satisfactory mean accuracy corresponds to values which are correct within ± 0.002. Now, if we take the value A which represents the largest divergence from the

mean 0·260, that is to say 0·282, we can see that the difference
0·022 represents a divergence of 0·003 in the value of i, which
is not very far off from the acceptable value 0·002. The sole
and exceptional divergence of 0·038 observed for the wound of
10 sq. cm. indicates that, when wounds inferior to this dimension are dealt with, the preponderant role of epithelization
destroys the accord which characterizes the phenomenon as a
whole: contraction *plus* epithelization. We already know
(Fig. 19, p. 87) that small wounds, just as very large ones, no
longer show the marked differences in their indices exhibited
by the majority of lesions between 10 and 150 sq. cm. for the
age of twenty.

But there is a better way to convince ourselves of the value
of the coefficient A. It consists in computing it for different
ages. Inasmuch as it is precisely the age which interests us,
we can in this way make the crucial experiment. The calculation of A for 30 years and for 40 years gives the figures of
the table on page 153. It will be noticed that the columns are
shorter than those of the preceding table (20 years). This
is due to the fact that the index, as may be remembered (see
p. 87) remains constant above a certain area. The coefficient
A being the product of the index i by the square root of the
area would have increased indefinitely beyond this limit and
would have become meaningless. We are therefore obliged to
keep within the limits imposed by the variations of i.

An examination of the figures in the columns 3 and 5 (values
of the coefficient $A = i\sqrt{S}$) shows that the constancy is in the
first case as good as, and in the second case better than, for the
values corresponding to the age of twenty. Indeed, the maximum divergence for 20 years was 0·038, whereas for 30 years
it is only 0·025 and for 40 years 0·006. The maximum divergences from the mean values are 0:022, 0·018, and 0·003
respectively. Considering that we are dealing with biological
phenomena, in which the same precision as in physical
phenomena cannot be obtained, that we have not taken into
account the causes of error enumerated above, and that,
moreover, it was especially important to put in evidence the

differences between mean values, it can be admitted that the coefficient A is very close to the activity constant of reparation within the accepted limits. The relative *maximum* errors

1	2	3	4	5
Area of the wound	Index i 30 years	Coefficient A 30 years	Index i 40 years	Coefficient A 40 years
sq. cm.				
80	0·0200	0·180	—	—
70	0·0220	0·184	—	—
60	0·0250	0·194	—	—
50	0·0275	0·194	0·0200	0·141
40	0·0310	0·196	0·0225	0·143
30	0·0375	0·205	0·0260	0·143
25	0·0400	0·200	0·0290	0·145
20	0·0465	0·207	0·0325	0·145
15	0·0525	0·204	0·0380	0·147
10	0·0625	0·198	0·0450	0·142
Mean value		0·198		0·144

expressed as a percentage of the mean value are 8·5 per cent in the first case (20 years), 9 per cent in the second (30 years), and 2 per cent in the third (40 years). These errors are inferior to those accepted for the index and are certainly less than those which affect the majority of measurements performed on living organisms.

Basing ourselves on the values of i for intermediary ages, we finally obtain the following mean values of A:

20 years	25 years	30 years	32 years	40 years
$A = 0·260$	0·225	0·198	0·188	0·144

We had only two patients of fifty under observation. They

gave the value of 0·103 for A. One single case for sixty: $A=0·08$; and only one case also for ten years of age: $A=0·4$. These values are therefore very doubtful. Fig. 27 expresses these results.

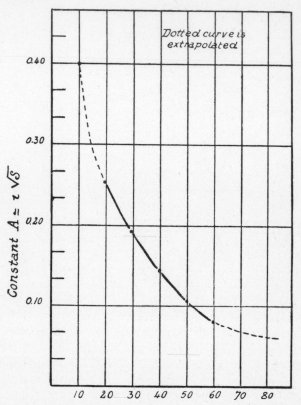

FIG. 27. COEFFICIENT 'A' AS A FUNCTION OF THE AGE OF THE PATIENT

What do these figures mean? It is extremely simple. These values of constant A signify that, if a child of ten will cicatrize a wound of 20 sq. cm. in twenty days (I purposely take an arbitrary round number), a man of twenty will cicatrize a wound of the same dimension in thirty-one days (20 is in the

DATE		PATIENT'S NAME	

Record of Calls

DATE	PATIENT'S NAME

same ratio to 31 as 0·26 to 0·40), a man of thirty, in forty-one days; a man of forty, in fifty-five days; a man of fifty, in seventy-eight days; and a man of sixty, in a hundred days. A wounded man, forty years old, therefore cicatrizes at a rate which is almost twice as slow (exactly 1·8 times) as that of a man of

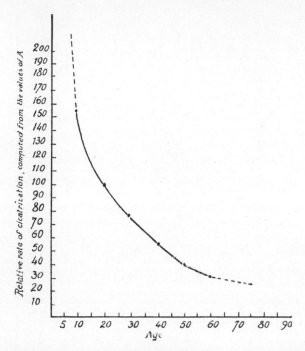

FIG. 28. RELATIVE RATE OF CICATRIZATION COMPUTED FROM CONSTANT 'A'

twenty. And a child of ten cicatrizes five times more quickly than a man of sixty. If the activities of cicatrization are referred to that of the age of twenty taken as the unit (100) the curve shown in Fig. 28 is obtained. This, like the preceding one, clearly shows the very rapid decrease of this activity in the first years of life and the tendency to reach a low and constant value towards the end of life.

Now, when a wound cicatrizes, what does it do? It effectuates a piece of work. Just as a mason closes up a breach in a wall, nature repairs a breach in our organism. When we measure the *velocity* at which this work is accomplished, by means of the sideral, physical time, we observe that it is very great at the beginning of life, slower at the middle and slower still towards the end of life. We can see on Fig. 28 that if 100 represents the velocity at twenty years of age, at thirty it is only 76 and at sixty 31. But it is expressed by 155 at ten years of age. It is therefore not constant with respect to our unit of measurement, the 24-hour day. *At different ages it takes different lengths of time to accomplish* THE SAME AMOUNT OF WORK: the cicatrization of one square centimetre of a wound.

On the other hand, it is possible to evaluate time by referring to a travelled distance or to a work done, if one is reasonably sure that the speed of displacement has been constant in the interval or if the workman has not changed the rhythm of his movements. We often employ expressions such as: the time to go to the post office, the time to dress, the time to write a page. In olden days, the hours of a trained labourer, working regularly, were often estimated by the work accomplished, for instance by the area mowed. Supposing he cuts, on an average, two hundred and fifty square yards an hour. If he has worked four hours we know that he has cut a thousand square yards. But if we have no watch and do not know how long he has worked, the measurement of the mowed area, two thousand square yards, for example, enables us to conclude that he has worked eight hours. We have therefore measured time by the amount of work performed. Consequently, if we reason in the same way for the work represented by the cicatrization of a wound, we can measure sideral time in units of physiological time.

An objection immediately imposes itself. We have just demonstrated that this work is accomplished at different velocities at different moments of our life. We are therefore no longer under the required condition. Not only is it impossible for us to affirm that the work has been accomplished at a constant rate of speed but we demonstrate precisely the contrary. We are here facing an absolute contradiction. This contradiction, however, is more apparent than real. Indeed, on what do we base ourselves to say that the velocity of repair is not uniform? We base ourselves on *physical* time, on the regular rhythm of our clocks. We therefore implicitly admit that this rhythm is invariable. But if, as was pointed out in the preceding chapter, this rhythm ceased to be uniform for any reason whatsoever, we could not know it and we would measure our phenomenon by means of a variable, elastic unit, which would destroy all the value of our conclusions. We would have no means of ascertaining whether the velocity of cellular reparation or that of the flow of the time employed to measure it, fluctuates.

Now, this unit, in which we have complete confidence, and to which we conventionally attribute an absolute rigidity and undeformability, is borrowed from our inorganic material universe. The use of this unit for measuring the evolution of our physiological and psychological ego is practical, but is it legitimate? As we have before remarked, there is a difference between the physical, sideral time based on the co-ordination of our sense impressions, but which remains nevertheless outside us, and our human duration which is a constituent of our ego as much as the space in which we evolve. It is our intelligence which 'thinks' the world. Our consciousness is born, ages, and dies. But in coming to life it inherits an enormous quantity of observations relative to this world which have been accumulated by preceding consciences and transmitted by word or by letter. It is this tradition which enables it to acquire the notion of the continuity of the universe.[1] It is this tradition which enables us to see and to locate ourselves in the world. A unique, isolated consciousness, without contact with those which have preceded it, would have very different notions. Our short and fragmentary human duration

[1] And many other 'notions' also, which our intelligence, our science have proved to be false or, if one prefers, relative; for example, the notion of the vertical, the trajectory in a straight line, the parallelism of two plumb-lines, etc.

is dependent on our organism as a whole, as well as the *notion* of this duration which is characterized by a discrepancy with the notion of uniform duration of inert things. Sideral, physical time perhaps also characterizes evolutions, but of such colossal duration that, in comparison to ours, it can be considered as infinite. We measure it by certain periodical phenomena such as the rotation of the earth around its axis, and without being able to verify our assertion, we conclude that it flows uniformly. This is perhaps an illusion due to the fact that we can perceive only a limited portion of a curve. Its radius of curvature might be so gigantic that it appears to us as a straight line. As we shall see later on, it is perhaps also because we conceive it as a wave front or an 'envelope' surface, which borrows its reality from the infinity of curves or determining elementary surfaces underlying it. It would be the *time of species* as opposed to *individual time*. The time of tissue-cultures, of the generations of infusoria; the statistical, conceptual, uniform time, projected by us into the universe *but not lived*.

Be that as it may, it would seem logical to borrow a standard of time from our specific evolutive cycle, and to refer all our internal phenomena to this unit, which is no more arbitrary than the one we commonly employed up till now. We have inside of us a machine which registers time: i.e. our subconscience. We also have a machine which conceives time: our intelligence. The two mechanisms, though different, are based on memory. Our subconscience gives our intelligence a crude information: time seems to flow quicker in proportion as we age. Our intelligence, a reflection of the external universe, only reveals to us the time of things, which leaps from individual to individual, and flows uniformly. These two notions are correlated but not interchangeable.

Even to a superficial observer, our internal physiological time does not seem to flow at a constant rate within the frame of external sideral time. Real age, as we have seen, can differ from legal age. From a psychological point of view, the value of a day is not identical for ephemeral insects and for animals that live to be sixty years old. Even for one individual, this value seems to vary during the course of life. Our duration would therefore be, in a certain measure, independent of sideral time. Each human being constitutes a universe in a state of continuous transformation. It is the rate of this transformation which can be considered as characteristic of our brief specific duration, of our physiological time itself, inseparable from our consciousness.

In short, seeing that this physiological time is truly our own, an interior time, and that humoral reactions and vital phenomena as a whole are governed by it more than by the rhythm of the earth's rotation; seeing that, in all likelihood, it is from our physiological reactions as a whole that we derive our notion of time which is inseparable from these reactions, since we must admit that consciousness is conditioned by them, we are authorized to carry to its logical conclusion the reasoning which motivated this digression and which brings us to the comparison of sideral time with physiological time. We are authorized to do it, not only by logic, but, what is more convincing, by experiments also. M. Marcel François, in a communication presented by Prof. Piéron at the Société de Biologie, entitled 'Sur l'influence de la température interne sur notre appreciation du temps',[1] concerns himself with the question of whether the perception of time is influenced by the increase in velocity of our internal chemical reactions. In order to verify this, he exposed patients to high-frequency currents (short waves). The test consisted in striking a Morse key three times a second—or rather the number of times which corresponded to a personal estimation of three per second—before and after a diathermic application. After the application, the internal temperature rose about 0·6° C. on an average (between 0·4° and 1° C.). He observed an acceleration in the temporal standard, *corresponding to a shortening in the appreciation of time, in respect to the increase in temperature.* This is in conformity with what might have been expected from the application of Van't Hoff's acceleration coefficient

[1] *C.R. Soc. Biol.*, vol. 98, p. 152 (1928).

in chemical reactions. These experiments led him to a value of this coefficient comprised between 2·75 and 2·85. This is a satisfactory accord—if one takes into account the difficulties of the experiment and the small difference in temperature— with the mean value of 2·5 for an increase of 10° C. (It may be remembered that I mentioned (page 98) experiments made at the Rockefeller Institute on cold-blooded animals (crocodiles) which clearly demonstrate the influence of the Van't Hoff coefficient in the cicatrization of wounds.) M. François' interesting results were entirely confirmed and extended by Hoagland in 1933.[1] Finally Wahl, Grabenberger, and Kolmus published very curious facts which also confirm our thesis and establish the chemical nature of the mechanisms which result in our psychological appreciation of time. When studying bees, ants, and termites, trained to come at a certain hour and take their food, the authors ascertained, by modifying the temperature, that an increase in temperature forced these insects to shorten the interval of time between two meals. This is the equivalent of an apparent dilatation of the time perceived by them. A decrease in temperature brought about a contrary effect. There can therefore be no doubt as to the nature of these phenomena.[2] The comparison of these two series of experiments demonstrates clearly the relation between the rate of cicatrization of wounds and the psychological appreciation of time. They both rest in last analysis on *a chemical basis*. There is no break of continuity in the chain of our reasoning, every link of which derives its solidity from an experimental confirmation.

Consequently, when we refer to sideral time as being the canvas on which the pattern of our existence is spread, we notice that the time needed to effectuate a certain unit of physiological work of repair is about four times greater at fifty than at ten years of age. *Everything, therefore, occurs as if*

[1] H. Hoagland, *Pace-makers in Relation to Aspects of Behaviour.* MacMillan, New York, 1935.

[2] This information was given to me by Prof. Piéron, to whom I express my thanks.

sideral time flowed four times faster for a man of fifty than for a child of ten. It is evident, on the other hand, that from a psychological point of view many more things happen to a child in a year than to an old man. The year therefore seems much longer to the child, and it is probable that the figures established—the constant *A*—enable us to realize quantitatively, not only by how much our physiological activity decreases, but also by how much physical time is apparently accelerated in respect to ourselves.

Thus, we find that when we take physiological time as a unit of comparison, physical time no longer flows uniformly. This affirmation revolts one if the words are taken in a literal sense. But we pointed out in the preceding chapter that if the expression 'flow of time' is in current use, it is nevertheless entirely false and does not correspond to a reality. We have seen that time is inseparable from space and matter and that the four-dimensional continuum, in conformity to the relative concept, is alone capable of furnishing a satisfactory frame for our universe. When, therefore, we say that physical time measured by means of a unit borrowed from our physiological time, no longer flows uniformly, it simply means that it does not *seem* to flow uniformly. At the bottom of our consciousness we perceive a discrepancy between the notion of our external time, without beginning or end, based on our science, our past experience or inherited documents, in other words between the notion of the uniform time of species, and the notion of individual, sensed time, limited by birth and death, which corresponds to the elementary curves of short period and variable velocity.

We can separate these two notions by an intellectual effort, but *physiological* time alone has a reality with respect to us. The envelope curve—the uniform sideral time—is perhaps nothing else but the resultant of the infinity of elementary curves, just as a light wave, or rather the wave front, is the perceptible resultant of the elementary group of waves given out by a luminous source, as shown in Fig. 29.

The envelope wave expands spherically, and each of its

vibrating points becomes in turn the centre of an elementary spherical wave, according to Huyghen's conception. The uniformity of external physical time would thus be a simple concept resting in last analysis on an infinity of individual non-uniform elements, the continuity of which is assured by memory and tradition.

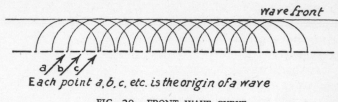

Each point a, b, c, etc. is the origin of a wave

FIG. 29. FRONT WAVE CURVE

It is evident that we do not intend to establish a parallel between the propagation of light waves and time. We have simply tried to clarify the notion of 'envelope'. A parallel could only exist provided each elementary wave issuing from a vibrating centre were damped in such a way as to progress more rapidly at the start than at the end. The discrepancy between the order of magnitude of the small individual waves and that of the envelope bubble is so great that the observer who perceives only the latter ignores its origin. Just as an observer of the universe cannot perceive the difference between the two times unless he succeeds in finding an internal standard of time: the physiological time defined above.

It seems to me that the extension of this notion of physiological time to the notion of appreciation of time is legitimate. On the one hand, our appreciation of time is one of the properties of our consciousness, and our consciousness is dependent on our physiological cellular reactions. It is therefore logical to admit that all slowing up of the activity of these reactions must result in a modification of our appreciation of time. We have demonstrated the fact that such was the case and, on the other hand, we know that time seems to flow more quickly as we grow older. This is a commonplace observation which is at least qualitatively in good accord with our experiments and our reasoning. Thus only the *quantitative* accord might be questioned, and we will take this up later.

It may be rightly objected that not all biological phenomena are slowed up by age in the same proportion as cellular activity. The answer to this is that it is necessary to differentiate between fundamental biological phenomena and the others. Phenomena such as cicatrization and cellular proliferation, which are life itself, i.e. the edification of living matter, must not be confused with certain physico-chemical phenomena which underlie our biological activities but which, as was shown at the beginning of this book, are different in many ways. If, for instance, one objects that the velocity of the nervous influx or irritability as a function of time— measured by 'chronaxy'—is far from being modified by age in the same proportion, one can answer that irritation is a property of living matter which is fundamental in that it determines the conditions of muscle and nerve action, but which is, however, less fundamental than the manufacture of the cells themselves. Irritability is an epiphenomenon. Cellular proliferation is the basic phenomenon of the building up of living matter. The remarkable notion of chronaxy, so ably developed by the French physiologist Lapicque, should be no more influenced by age than fundamental phenomena such as the beating of the heart, for example. On the other hand, it can be plausibly admitted that hematopoiesis—the manufacture of red blood cells—is affected in the same proportion as cicatrization. The measurement of chronaxy cannot give any information concerning the age of the organism because it is only the measurement of a property of living matter and not a measurement of the vital activity of the cells. Tissue-cultures live and cicatrize their wounds without a nervous system.

A more serious objection is that the impression of the more rapid flight of time is simply due to the varying ratio of the length of the time unit—a year, for instance—to the total duration of life. For example, a year *seems* longer to a child of five than to a man of fifty because it represents the fifth of his existence, whereas it represents only the fiftieth part of the life of the older man. This would imply a notion of time based on memory, and a permanent subconscious confrontation of the time which flows with the time elapsed since birth. This objection is important because it is full of common sense. Let us examine it with the attention it deserves.

First of all, what can be the mechanism of this memory? We are not speaking of the memory of precise facts standing out against the moving background of our existence, but of the registration of the very motion of this mobile background. It is somewhat as if we were in a theatre watching the play of actors—representing our internal perceptions projected outside of us—and as if the scenery were being shifted always in the same direction, unwinding itself on the right and being rolled up on the left. From a mechanical point of view it is easy to conceive that the more canvas is wound the larger will be the diameter of the roll and the greater will be the velocity. But this is much too crude a comparison. Can we find among known biological facts a basis which would allow us to visualize this quantitative recording of past time? Indeed we can, for we know that ageing introduces chemical modifications into our organism, the effect of which is progressively to increase the toxicity of our serum, that mirror of our physiological reactions. This fact stands out clearly in the experiments of Carrel and Ebeling, described in detail on p. 116. There is, consequently, an accumulation of toxic products in the fluids of our organism. We know, on the other hand, that the activity of physiological reparation evolves parallel to this phenomenon and that the curves representing the growth-index of tissue-cultures and the index of cicatrization assume very nearly the same aspect. The two phenomena can almost be superposed. It may be inferred that they are basically very similar. The older the individual from which a serum proceeds, the more toxic his serum becomes for tissue-cultures and the slower will the individual cicatrize. Here is a biological fact which indicates that each year in passing *leaves an indelible trace in us*, just as in a motor-car every turn of the wheels registers in the speedometer a figure which is added on to the preceding figures. Nature does not dispose of mechanical systems such as speedometers, but the result is approximately the same. It seems difficult to call upon another procedure for the explanation of the existence of this type of memory, for there can be no question of a mechanism identical with that of our sense memory which retains and easily evokes events registered by our senses, but without respecting the dimensions of time. A proof of this is given by dreams in which the scale of time is often strangely contracted. But, when the registration of the flight of time is concerned there can only be question of a passive, subconscious memory, of physico-chemical or chemical nature, which would be only one of the manifestations of ageing, and the very foundation of our notion of duration.

Should this really be the case we would have answered the objection, for we would have demonstrated that the fact of admitting an estimation of the apparent length of a year, based on the comparison of the number of years gone by since birth, would imply a subconscious totalizing system which might well be one of the psychological manifestations of the physiological and chemical transformations introduced by age. Instead of eliminating the objection we would, on the contrary, have incorporated it into the totality of phenomena which are correlative to ageing. But the whole question would still remain hypothetical.

To confirm the reasoning as a whole or, at least, bolster up its probability by facts, the two series of calculations used to express quantitatively the apparent shortening of duration of one year, based, the first, on the coefficient A of physiological activity, the second, on the value of a year expressed in fractions of the age of a man, *should coincide at least approximately*. If only the order of magnitude of the shortening were the same in both cases, it would supply an impressive argument in favour of the thesis expounded in this book.

Nothing is easier than to confront the two hypotheses. If

age intervenes numerically in the estimation of the duration of a year, the curve representing the value of one year for each age can be drawn by simply plotting as ordinates the values of the reciprocal of the ages plotted as abscissae. We have stated that the year of a five-year-old child seems long to him because it represents *one-fifth* of his existence, or 0·20. To a man of twenty, a year (*one-twentieth* of his existence or 0·05) will seem shorter in the same proportion as 1 to 4. For a man of fifty it will be only *one-fiftieth* or 0·02. To the latter, time will seem to flow ten times faster than to the child of five. We thus obtain the solid curve of Fig. 30. It is a very simple curve, an equilateral hyperbola, the branches of which are asymptotic of the axes of co-ordinates and which answers to the elementary equation: $xy = 1$ or $y = \dfrac{1}{x}$. Let us now super-pose this curve on that of Fig. 28, p. 155. The values of the abscissae (age) coincide. For the ordinates we must keep the scales comparable; namely the figures, although different, must be proportional to those of the preceding diagram. We obtain the dotted curve of Fig. 30 and we notice at once a similarity which, if not absolute, is nevertheless very remark-able. There is no complete coincidence, but it is indisputable that the aspect is nearly the same between the ages of fifteen and sixty. We must not forget that, as we said on p. 154, our experimental figures are doubtful before twenty and after fifty years of age.

Does this mean that the reactions registered by age inside of us, faithful witnesses of the flight of years, evolve according to a hyperbolic law? We cannot affirm this, for it would imply the admission that no other process enters into play, and nothing authorizes at present the formulation of such a postu-late. We may, however, note that such curves are not infre-quent in chemistry: the dissociation curve of Nernst (iso-thermal dissociation) is precisely an equilateral hyperbola. This curve gives the number of ions produced in a solution by dissociation, as a function of the concentration in mole-cules. It shows that the phenomenon decreases when the

concentration increases, following a hyperbolic law. We do
not wish to draw any conclusion from this. We simply

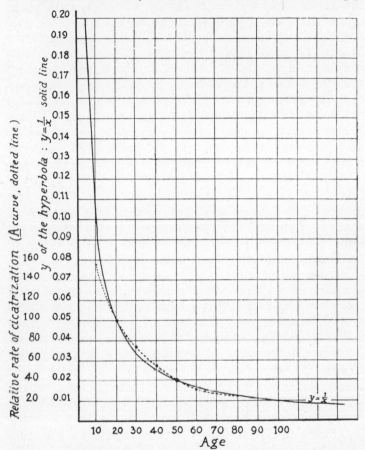

FIG. 30. RELATIVE RATE OF CICATRIZATION AND APPRECIATION
OF THE VALUE OF TIME AS A FUNCTION OF THE AGE

wanted to recall this classical example so as to remind one
that chemical phenomena obeying this law exist.

*This concordance between a curve obtained by quantitative
experiments on the cicatrization of wounds, a curve which*

summarizes the results of a great number of measurements made without any preconceived idea, and a curve obtained by expressing quantitatively the consequences of a simple reasoning based on common sense and psychological observation is very striking.

A year is thus physiologically and psychologically much longer for a child than for its parents. Supposing the parents to be forty years old and the child ten, one year will represent for the child about the same length of time as three (derived from constant A) or four (derived from the hyperbola) years for the parents. If the child is younger the difference will be still more marked, but we have no experimental figures wherefrom it could be computed. The hyperbola of Fig. 30 might furnish them, but it is probable that a satisfactory accord can be obtained only between the extreme limits of fifteen and sixty years of age. The diagram of Fig. 31 represents the apparent values of one year at different ages with respect to its value at the age of twenty, taken as unit. It can be seen that we limited ourselves to the age of ten.

There is nothing, moreover, to prove that the hyperbolical rate is valid beyond this age. It is impossible to speak of the notion of time in a very young child and it is extremely probable that the rate of cicatrization is not increased in the proportion indicated by the curve. The extrapolation, represented by the vertical branch which attains an infinite velocity for o years of age, has no meaning. No more meaning than the expression, o years of age, itself; for should one start counting it from the beginning of the time of the fecundation of the egg or from birth? These are purely intellectual bouts.

The region of maximum curvature, that of our material and conscious existence, is situated exactly midway between infinite velocity and infinite slowness, astride on the hyperbolic axis which cuts the curve at the point corresponding to thirty-one years and a half. It is impossible not to notice that for a pure relativist it would be very tempting to assimilate every living being to a simple deformation of the four-dimensional space-time continuum so as to explain the non-uniform flow of our time as compared to universal time.

Young and old, united in the same space, live in a separate
universe where the value of time is radically different. Peda-
gogues and psychologists do not seem as yet to have taken
into account the considerable importance of this disaccord.
Obviously, the manner in which this could be done is by no
means evident. But this is another problem.

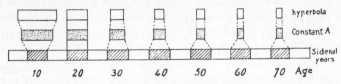

FIG. 31. RELATIVE VALUES OF OUR APPRECIATION OF THE DURATION
OF ONE SIDERAL YEAR, COMPUTED FROM THE CONSTANT 'A' (SECOND ROW),
AND FROM THE HYPERBOLA (FIRST ROW), WITH RESPECT TO THE AGE
OF TWENTY TAKEN AS REFERENCE

Thus there is a physiological time which has no signification
excepting for organisms capable of being born, of ageing, and
of dying normally. This word 'normally' contains in substance the greater part of unsolved biological problems. It
implies, for instance, the action of the organic regulating
mechanisms which establish the fundamental difference
between the healthy normal growth of cells and the abnormal,
anarchical growth of cancerous cells, between an immortal
tissue-culture and an individual who is born, lives, and dies.

Between a malignant tumour and a healing wound which
cicatrizes by rapid cellular proliferation let loose in the healthy
tissue by the wound itself there is, barring the morphological
difference of the cells, only the following difference: proliferation stops instantaneously when reparation is ended in a
healthy flesh, whereas a cancerous tissue ignores this regulating mechanism and continues to proliferate until death
follows. Similarly, when a tissue-culture is cut in two and
placed in a fresh drop of nutritive medium after washing, the
cells, which proliferate slowly in the organism, are taken with
a frenzy of growth and reproduce with great rapidity. We
have seen that a tissue-culture two square millimetres in size
doubles its volume in forty-eight hours indefatigably and

indefinitely. The elimination by washing of the toxic waste products due to the metabolism, suppresses ageing in this fragment of tissue, just as for cancer cells, individual physiological time no longer exists or rather is blended into sideral time, 'envelope' time. Like all animal species considered as a whole in their secular evolution, this little piece of flesh registers only the uniformly flowing physical time. Each of its cells, considered separately, probably evolves in the physiological time, the same as all individuals. But everything occurs as if continuous flowing time, the 'wave front' time, which is perceptible to our intelligence but is not *our* time, played a much more important though more mysterious role than individual time. The death of the individual is of no importance. It is the species which counts, and we cannot know if the species is endowed with consciousness. Just as the personality of a molecule is abolished in a crystal, so does the individual disappear in the evolution of organized beings, drowned in the mysterious stream which he contributes to form.

The conclusion at which we arrive of a 'granular', variable, individual time, differing from the continuous, integral, universal time, has nothing in it which should surprise us. A genial intelligence could have foreseen it, for, since more than a century ago, science has tended to destroy the palpable notion of continuity and to replace it by the impalpable one of discontinuity. Our senses, which are the intermediaries between the universe and ourselves, translate discontinuity into continuity, air pulsations into sound, groups of waves, accompanying photons, into light. The first success—foreseen by Democritus—was the demonstration of the granular, fragmentary nature of matter. Imperceptible molecules and atoms give us, by reason of their immense number in any body whatsoever, the impression of continuity. The second was the discovery of the electron, which established the granular nature of electricity. The third was the discovery of the quantum of action, which destroyed our clear idea of continuity of energy. Matter, electricity, energy, all our material universe, are but 'envelope' manifestations of statistical phenomena resulting from the play of isolated elements which are themselves deprived of dimensions. There is therefore nothing astonishing in the fact that we are brought to the conclusion that the very essence of time is granular and that its continuity is only the statistical appearance given it by individuals so as to class all the other external statistical phenomena in their consciousness and in their memory.[1]

We know that the major laws which govern our material bodies—Newton's law, the electrostatic law of Coulomb, and others—apply only at a certain scale, and cease to apply at the electronic scale. We see that the law of flow, the succession of our internal phenomena, is also different from the law of flow of the external phenomena of the universe. Must one consider this fact as the indication of a difference of magnitude between our short individual period and the immense periods of the universe? Must we see a proof of the existence of such periods? Who knows? All that we can say at present is that our crude language, lacking appropriate words, translates this knowledge into improper, inadequate expressions such as:

[1] It is evidently absurd to speak of 'the very essence of time'. Space, time, energy, are beyond our terminology. However, to distinguish between these two concepts, of continuity and discontinuity, we are forced to employ current expressions. All our experience and all our science lead us to the admission that continuity exists nowhere, and that one of the roles of consciousness is to manufacture continuity from discontinuity. The notion of continuity is essentially human. It is normal that this tendency of our consciousness should have been applied to time as well as to the material universe. However, if all our universe is discontinuous we nevertheless observe the existence of many phenomena the continuity of which is indisputable and likewise based on elementary discontinuous phenomena. The persistence of species, for instance, or the manifestations of 'the spirit of the hive', in bees as well as in ants and termites. M. Jean Rostand could give us many examples borrowed from insects. Here, also, something continuous is born in our consciousness from discontinuity, but from a discontinuity of *quite another order of magnitude* than electronic, quantic, or even molecular discontinuity. There is nothing shocking in speaking of our physiological time as a constitutive element of our concept of a uniformly flowing time. The latter is perhaps a mere product of our intelligence. It is, moreover, possible that outside of the major tendencies cited above (persistence of species, etc.), thought alone is continuous. But this would be very difficult to prove.

'There are two species of time', or 'Physiological time does not
flow uniformly like physical time.' We must not be duped
by these words; we must not let ourselves be bound by them.
We must try to perceive, beyond them, the reality which they
vainly strive to translate: 'The flow which does not imply a
flowing thing, and the passage which does not presuppose
states through which one passes', as says Bergson, who was
led to conceive different durations diversely rhythmed, when
living species are concerned. But this was only a hypothesis.
In pages 58 and 61 of *Durée et Simultanéité*, he arrives, by pure
reasoning, at conclusions very similar to ours, in the sense
that he develops the idea of 'the unity of an impersonal time
in which all things flow' and which is the result of the time
registered simultaneously by all human consciences. One
feels that he lacked the clear experimental facts capable of
substantiating his reasoning, i.e. the difference between universal time and individual physiological time. But his in-
tuition and immense talent had almost supplied the deficiency,
even though he was finally led to admit a unique universal
time. His intelligence was apparently revolted, if one may
say so, by the fragility of deductions resting on no measurable
phenomenon.

The fact that we conceive the universal time as a mere
conceptual envelope of our physiological, individual time,
does not mean that we intend to affirm that it would no longer
exist if all life were swept from the universe. Let us pass over
the absurdity of the expression: 'Time which exists', on which
we have already insisted, and define our meaning. From
all that precedes, it seems to us that the reader must have
already disengaged the fact that our universe, the universe
 which we perceive and conceive, exists *as such* only in our
consciousness. Let man, his senses and his memory, be
suppressed, and the universe is reduced to vibrations, to
forces, to velocities deprived of the familiar aspects which we
lend them by placing ourselves in their path. We gather
them and transform them by means of our sense organs. We
 translate them in our consciousness and baptize them Reality.

This is our only reality. But there is, behind this shadow, the object which projects it, and which ever since Plato we have vainly tried to conceive. The intersideral spaces are black and cold. 'Energy quanta' circulate through them in every direction and in infinite numbers.[1] Without an adequate receptor to intercept, accumulate, totalize and transform them, they are nothing but quanta. In the absence of human beings, light, heat, sound, do not exist as such. In the absence of radio sets, waves emitted by the broadcasting stations are inexistent for us. Each one of our senses acts as a receiving set and translates for our consciousness the silent, invisible, and abstract message of the quanta of energy. It is in this sense that we have occasionally called our physiological time real time. It is owing to this time that the summation of quanta takes place in our brain, and that we perceive the universe as we perceive it. The other, the time of things, the time of the obscure and mute universe, unknown and un-knowable, has no more reality for us than radio waves in the absence of receiving sets. 'In this time without duration, events could not succeed each other, nor things subsist, nor beings age' (Bergson). If it governs us as a combination of atoms and molecules, it does not govern us as a living individual destined to die. It is, on the contrary, our physiological time which enables us to conceive, through our intelligence, the uniformity of flow impossible of perception. Should it be demonstrated some day that universal time can be resolved into quanta, then the same would be true of our physiological time. The quantum of physiological time would then be a function of the period of our existence, and would be different for each species. The picture of a curve, or of a wave front, which we have proposed in order to explain our concept of universal time would, in this case, be materially strengthened. But this draws us into a speculative domain, and that is pre-cisely what we have tried to avoid.

．　　　．　　　．　　　．　　　．

[1] Before Planck and Einstein one would have said, 'waves or vibrations of ether'.

We have now come to the end of this study, which has led us from the biological problem in general to the notion of time. The first part of this book can be compared to a trip in an aeroplane at a low altitude above a poorly explored country of varying aspects. From on high, without going through the fatigues and deceptions of the explorer, we have been able to realize the enormous and various difficulties which he would encounter on his way. Then, choosing with care our landing-place, we alighted in a region more easy of access than the others, though still barren. We then reported in detail the material labour of the pioneer, the clearing of the land, the organization of the conquered ground, the tracing of roads leading to already colonized regions, the blazing of trails towards the unknown. Once this programme accomplished, we again stepped into the aeroplane and rose to a greater height, losing sight of the details but embracing in a single sweep of the eye our universe and the relations between certain external causes and their subjective effects. Chance decreed that some of our experiments were of a nature to throw a little light on the fundamental notions which form the frame of our concepts. We deducted therefrom a few conclusions which seemed to us legitimate. We do not doubt that we will be criticized for it. And yet, is it not logical to try to throw a bridge between the external world and our consciousness, considering that we can now approach the problems which have preoccupied men for centuries: problems of space, of matter, of time? The pure physicist cannot do this for, *a priori*, he neglects consciousness, which is not of his domain. Progress in this direction can therefore come only by the path of biology.

The purely imaginary, philosophical concepts of olden days are outdistanced. Our ideas on matter are infinitely more mysterious than the wildest lucubrations of philosophers. We cannot, and will not, doubt the evidence of our senses, the indications of our instruments, and the deductions of our intelligence. We admit that the properties of things are due to the motion of elements which seem to have no existence outside of this motion. We ascertain that all reality can be traced back to a conjunction of space and time, that immobility is synonymous with nullity, and yet we hesitate, not without a certain hypocrisy, to look things in the face. We have been frightened of philosophy. We have been warned, and rightly so, against mere intellectual exercises. But now that science brings us back to measurable, concrete facts, which raise new problems, we are forced to attack them, if the conquests of the human mind are to continue, even though these problems have been listed sixty years ago amongst the 'untouchable' questions reserved for philosophers. We cannot help but smile nowadays when thinking of the ancient quarrels. There is no more room for such childishness, which only existed because of our ignorance and because, the problems being wrongly stated, the extrapolations were false. The modern experimental results have made a hecatomb of theories in 'ism'. A harvest of disturbing facts arises in their place. As they are solidly established, they can hardly give birth to quarrels, but in front of them, deprived of the magnificent confidence of our predecessors, we often feel our reason falter.

It must be admitted that these results have sometimes dashed the hopes prematurely expressed with great publicity by certain scientists of the last century who had given rein to their enthusiasm and sentimental convictions to the detriment of those primordial qualities of a scientist: prudence and humility. This cannot be helped. Our immense progress is measured principally by the fact that we now admit that we know nothing—or very little—and that it is quite possible that we shall never know much more. Our science will assuredly progress, and the material conditions of our existence will be transformed—I hesitate to say ameliorated. Day by day we will learn to use with greater skill the elements composed ultimately of pure velocity, that is to say, of space and time. But what benefit will our consciousness, which transforms these velocities into a universe, derive therefrom? How will our happiness be increased? These are vain questions. There is no doubt that a new era is beginning from a philosophical point of view. Those who are tempted to deny it need only pass in review the conquests of physics since the discovery of radio-activity. Whether they wish it or not, they will be obliged to admit that our brain has reduced the universe, as we said above, to velocities and accelerations; that is to say, to space and time. Even ether, the unreal reality which could give our predecessors the illusion of a substratum of phenomena, has been suppressed.[1] We find ourselves confronted by a world characterized by a number of statistical properties,[2] the resultant at our scale of different elementary phenomena. These elementary phenomena escape us because we ourselves are a statistical resultant. But it is they which are the Universe itself, the universe considered in the absence of Man.

Man is too curious not to ask himself whether the universe exists outside of him. He already agitated the question in olden days when his intelligence, genius, and faith were the only elements he possessed to solve this immense problem. We have progressed since Leibnitz and his monads, but we seem to travel in a closed circuit. One of two things: either we shall continue to accumulate facts which will raise an unsurmountable wall around us, or else we shall have the courage to climb to the top of the tower in which we imprison ourselves, so as to throw a circular glance around and take our bearings without any preconceived ideas. We never suspected, when we decided to abandon dialectics and philosophy and to lean exclusively on science, that the latter would lead us so rapidly to the edge of the abyss. We are the victims of a 'Cartesianism' pushed to the extreme limit, and now we are caught in our own trap. We must jump the fence or stay where we are. We will not be able to experiment on pure time and space by means of our beautiful instruments, nor can we apply to them the reasoning and rigorous laws which have no value outside of our presence. How shall we manage

[1] There are many excellent books on the subject. I have cited a few of them, but new ones appear continually in every country.

[2] One should read the admirable book of Ch. E. Guye on this subject, *L'Evolution physico-chimique*, to which I have already referred the reader (note, pp. 24, 27).

to suppress, in thought, this presence outside of which we cannot speak of reality?

So far, only mathematicians have dared to venture into the domain of the imponderable. They speak a language the symbols of which express solely pure ideas or relations. Thanks to this privilege they can explore the most abstract regions and emit daring theories without incurring the thunder of the enemies of philosophy, the rationalists. It must be admitted that mathematical methods possess a rigorousness never attained by ancient philosophers, which enables a greater number of men to reason with a seeming of truth. Yet, there as elsewhere, the value of the conclusions depends on the value and legitimacy of the premises and postulates, that is to say, on the genius of man and not on the rigour of the intermediate reasoning.

Nowadays our philosophers are mathematicians. Their aim, if not their ambition, is not to explain, but to translate quantitatively the facts perceived by our conscience. This is undoubtedly a marked progress. Nevertheless, the question now arises as to whether quantitative symbols will ever be able to express life, psychological phenomena in general, intelligence, and mathematical reasoning itself, including the principle of beauty which it so often embodies.

INDEX OF NAMES

2. 00